An Economic Model—
New Oil and Gas Supplies in the Lower 48 States

An Economic Model—
New Oil and Gas Supplies

in the Lower 48 States

Young Y. Kim
Russell G. Thompson

Gulf Publishing Company
Book Division
Houston, London, Paris, Tokyo

An Economic Model—
New Oil and Gas Supplies in the Lower 48 States

Library of Congress Catalog Card Number 78-53816

ISBN 0-87201-816-4

Contents

Preface

Achieving a desired balance between economic growth, energy independence, and environmental quality will require sound information with regard to future crude oil and natural gas supplies in the United States. This informational need is especially acute for the lower 48 states, where extensive exploration, development, and production has already occurred. It is supplies from this part of the country that will be the backbone for tiding the nation over in a transition from oil and gas to alternative energy sources. How much more drilling and additions to reserves can the nation expect at higher prices? How will these reserve additions be affected by modifications in tax provisions, such as forcing amortization of intangible drilling costs, rather than allowing current deductions as at present? Sound answers to these fundamental questions largely determine how fast the nation must (1) allow offshore development, (2) switch to coal for boiler fuel, (3) accelerate the construction of nuclear generating plants, or (4) increase payments for imported oil and gas.

Unfortunately, the weakest link in the endless congressional debate over an energy policy has been the economics of crude oil and natural gas supplies. The industry, which has a vast accumulation of basic data, has never had any incentive to synthesize this technical data into a comprehensive economic framework. In earlier years, there was really no need to make the synthesis because the public felt that cheap crude oil and natural gas supplies were endless; and in recent years, when the public has begun to realize it is *not* endless in supply, the industry has lost much of its credibility in the body politic. The Federal Energy Administration (FEA) resurrected one of the early studies by the National Petroleum Council as a stopgap measure, but for one reason or another, they never sought the necessary technical expertise to weld this resurrection into a sound supply model. Also, the FEA continued to depend on yesteryear's procedures of the U.S. Geological Survey (U.S.G.S.) for estimating reserve additions.

The U.S.G.S. has always proceeded as if statistical error in findings was the primary explanation for variations in reserve additions; they have almost totally ignored the effects of changes in prices and tax provisions. The U.S.G.S. has assumed a given set of prices and tax provisions (which they have never documented), and, in addition, has used undocumented functional relationships for mapping these prices and tax provisions (with their estimated finding rates) into reserve additions. All the public has generally been given is the values of the function; they have not been given the function and the values of its arguments. Thus, the public has been left completely in the dark as to what would happen to reserve additions and forthcoming supplies if changes occurred in the prices or tax provisions.

This study represents an initial effort to bring light into a critical policy-making area, where we, as a nation, have been in the dark far too long. Primary emphasis is directed at showing how both policy variables (e.g., oil and gas prices and tax provisions) and finding rates will affect reserve additions, production rates, and economic supplies. Our results show, for example, a range of reserve additions for natural gas varying from nearly zero under unfavorable taxes, prices, and finding rates to around 750 trillion cubic feet under favorable taxes, prices, and finding rates. This large range of reserve additions overwhelms the much smaller range of reserve additions (261 to 406 trillion cubic feet) estimated by the U.S.G.S., where taxes and prices are not varied. The fundamental result of the study is that supply clearly depends on government policy. Sound inputs and imaginative policies are the keystones for the nation to make a smooth transition from oil and gas to alternative energy sources, yet at the same time achieve a balance between economic growth, environmental quality, and energy independence.

Further work is needed to determine how responsive supplies of oil and gas from offshore and Alaska will be to price, tax provisions, and leasing schedules. Similar studies need to be made to evaluate the economics of synthetic supplies of oil and gas. Clarity of communications in all these studies would be improved greatly by an effort to (i) abstract the information in the computer models and (ii) summarize this information in statistically estimated equations. These statistically estimated equations would give the public explicit mathematical mappings—of the policy variables and finding rate projections—showing reserve additions, production rates, and economic supplies. Unfortunately, the $5,000 contract of the Texas Energy Advisory Council for this study did not allow us to complete these needed extensions. Hopefully, additional funding will be available in the future to further enlighten the public as to how supply depends on policy.

We are deeply indebted to the support of the Texas Energy Advisory Council and to the patient understanding of Dr. Milton Holloway, who directed the forecast activities of the Advisory Council at the time of this study and is now its Executive Director. The supply model has been transferred to the Advisory Council's computers and in the written words of Dr. Holloway to Dr. Howell, Director of The Energy Institute at the University of Houston:

> "We have installed this model on our own computer facilities, and with the documentation provided by Dr. Thompson, have been operating the model. The study has provided us with valuable estimates of crude oil and natural gas supplies in the future as an independent study but is also a crucial input to the econometric modeling of the Texas economy maintained in our office. Documentation to this model has been transferred to us and has been useful in operating the model,"— October 24, 1977.

In summary, successful model transfer and use has been accomplished in this study, as well as successful model development.

We are indebted to the American Petroleum Institute, the Federal Energy Administration, the Energy Research and Development Administration, the U.S. Geological Survey, the Mitchell Energy and Development Corporation, and the Shell Oil Company for their critical reviews and helpful comments. Appreciation is further due to Dr. James A. Calloway, Mr. Steve Stewart, and Mr. Raj Sodhi who were instrumental in developing an efficient computer program and an accurate final manuscript. Support for developing this efficient computer program was provided by the University of Houston's Energy Institute and Office of Public Affairs. Also, the review and editorial assistance was deeply appreciated of Dr. Lynn LaMotte, Dr. Archie McWhorter, and Ms. Lillian Nawalanic. In addition, the patient and accurate typing assistance of Mr. Steven Carlberg was instrumental in completing the final manuscript. However, any findings, conclusions, or recommendations are those of the authors and do not necessarily reflect the views of the assistants, reviewers, the Texas Energy Advisory Council, or the University of Houston.

Y. Y. Kim and Russell G. Thompson

June 1978

Purpose,
Methods and
Structure of the Model

Since the Arab Oil Embargo in the fall of 1973, uncertainty regarding future additions to crude oil and natural gas reserves and future production from these reserves at different government pricing and taxing policies has greatly slowed the development of a viable energy policy in the United States. Participants in the debate over uncertain oil and gas reserves have taken either the position of the consumers who refuse to believe the cheap reserves are gone or the position of the producers who refuse to make investments to expand oil and gas supplies at current low prices.

The polarity of these positions is illustrated by the dialogue between Dr. M. King Hubbert of the U.S. Geological Survey and Dr. Barry Commoner of Washington University. Dr. Commoner regards Dr. Hubbert's forecasts of oil and gas reserves (Hubbert, 1974) as gross underestimates because Hubbert uses declining historical trends in the finding rates for new oil and gas discoveries. Commoner claims our present oil shortage is not due to a scarcity of domestic oil but to the declining efforts of U.S. oil companies to find oil (Commoner, 1976).

Both Hubbert and Commoner are partially correct. Hubbert's diminishing finding rate reflects the principle of diminishing marginal returns in exploiting a fixed resource. However, as long recognized by economists, diminishing marginal returns are insufficient for forecasting the economic development and usage of a resource. This physical description of marginal productivity must be augmented with appropriate market prices and economic costs to find the profit-maximizing levels of resource development and production. Economically, the ultimate reserves developed and the corresponding supplies produced are functions of the prices received for crude oil and natural gas, prices paid for inputs used in exploration, development, and production, and tax provisions of state and national government.

The primary purpose of our study is to show how the fundamental economic and technical considerations in oil and gas exploration, development, and production may be synthesized into a comprehensive economic model of new crude oil and natural gas supplies in the lower 48 states. Our model is then used to show how forecasts of economically recoverable reserves, depletion rates, production paths, and economic supplies will be affected by different wellhead prices, depletion allowances, tax deductions, finding rates, and drilling capacity availabilities.

As in Hill's study for Texas (Hill, 1975), the fundamental driving force determining exploratory drilling, recoverable reserves, production rates, and economic supplies of oil and natural gas from newly found reserves is the maximization of profits, subject to the diminishing finding rate. In contrast to the studies of the National Petroleum Council (NPC, 1972) and the Federal Energy Administration (FEA, 1974, 1976), crude oil and natural gas are modeled as joint economic products, because higher gas prices increase the production of oil as well as gas, and higher oil prices increase the production of gas as well as oil.

Both NPC and FEA studies assumed exploratory drilling paths and production rates from new reserve additions. Our study derives the path of exploratory drilling investments and the rate of production from additions to reserves to maximize the net present value of investments in exploratory drilling. Our method differs fundamentally from the previous studies of natural gas supplies by MacAvoy and Pindyck (1973), Erickson and Spann (1971), Khazzoom (1971), and Epple (1975); statistical analyses of historical data were made to determine how higher natural gas prices would increase natural gas production. Statistical estimates of supply functions (quantity produced as a function of price) have large forecast errors when the price variable takes values far outside the range of historical observation. Also, statistical examinations of historical data are generally incapable of showing the consequences of major changes in government policy.

Epple's carefully constructed econometric model is based on the economic theory of production. His model accounts for the joint product characteristic of oil and gas production. Diminishing returns of exploratory activities, as well as prices after taxes and discounting considerations, were included in the specification of the model. However, Epple must assume a path of total cumulative exploratory wells to forecast total exploratory drilling footage and reserve additions for crude oil and natural gas. Exploratory drilling decision variables are endogenously derived as a part of the solution to the model developed in our study. Several additional differences are note-worthy: (1) API estimates of reserve additions were not adjusted for growth in reserves, as shown by Hubbert (1974); (2) important policy decision variables are not explicitly identified; and (3) a constant rate of production from new reserves was assumed.

Our study differs from Epple's in the following ways: (1) API estimates of reserve additions are adjusted for growth in reserves; (2) cumulative historical finds are statistically related to cumulative historical drilling footages to forecast the diminishing finding rate; (3) important policy variables are explicitly identified; and (4) a profit-maximizing model is used to forecast exploratory drilling, reserve additions, and supplies of oil and gas. The economic model shows how a profit-conscious oil and gas industry in the lower 48 states will explore for new reserves, develop reserve additions, and produce crude oil and natural gas for a wide range of economic conditions and policy considerations.

1.1 Mathematical Structure of the Supply Model

The profitability of a new exploratory venture is measured by the sum of the discounted value of the revenues from the venture less the discounted value of the costs incurred in the venture. This sum is called the net present value (NPV) of the venture; its general equation is developed in Equation (1-7).

Profitability of a new venture is significantly affected by the success of drilling for new fields in areas where neither gas nor oil has been produced before (exploratory drilling). The finding rate is derived from the function expressing cumulative reserves (Y) as a function of cumulative exploratory drilling footage (X):

$$Y = F(X) \tag{1-1}$$

The finding rate, $dY/dX = Y'$, is generally a monotonically decreasing function of cumulative exploratory drilling because of the law of diminishing returns.

If ΔX feet of new exploratory drilling are added to a cumulative drilling base of X_0, then new reserves will increase by ΔY:

$$\Delta Y = F(X_0 + \Delta X) - F(X_0) \tag{1-2}$$

An increase in reserves (ΔY) may be exploited at different rates of depletion (d). Increasing the rate of depletion of a given reserve base requires increasingly greater levels of drilling to economically develop a field (development drilling). Development drilling footage may be expressed as a function of the depletion rate (d):

$$D = g(d) \tag{1-3}$$

Development drilling generally increases at an increasing rate, resulting in increases in the depletion rate. Additional total drilling footage (ΔZ) is the sum of additional exploratory drilling footage (ΔX) plus additional development drilling footage (ΔD):

$$\Delta Z = \Delta X + \Delta D \tag{1-4}$$

Total investment in drilling (I) may be approximated as a constant multiple (λ) of additional total drilling footage:

$$I = \lambda\Delta X + \lambda\Delta D = \lambda\Delta Z \tag{1-5}$$

In our study, production in the tth year (q_t) after the start of production from a new discovery is assumed to be the following function of incremental reserves (ΔY) and the depletion rate (d):

$$q_t = \Delta Yd(1-d)^{t-1} \tag{1-6}$$

This production path assumes the increment to reserves (ΔY) will be depleted at an exponential decline rate. Clearly, $\Sigma_{t-1}^{\infty} q_t = \Delta Y$. However, for practical purposes production is discontinued at year T_a where additional production revenues do not cover operating costs. Production in years at the economic margin of profitability for finding new reserves and depleting a given reserve, $t = 1$, $t = 2$, . . . , $t = T_a$, may be represented by the vector, $q = (q_1, q_2, \ldots, q_{Ta})$. The NPV of an exploratory drilling venture may be expressed in the following functional way.

$$NPV = h(q, I; \alpha), \tag{1-7}$$

where $\alpha = $ a vector of parametric constants.

The vector α of parametric constants includes the product price (α_1), tax provisions (α_2), discount rate (α_3), royalty rate (α_4), exploratory drilling costs (α_5), development drilling costs (α_6), and production costs (α_7). Because both q and I are functions of X and d, the necessary conditions for a maximum are:

$$\partial NPV/\partial d = (\partial h\, \partial q/\partial q\, \partial d) + (\partial h\, \partial I\, \partial D/\partial I\, \partial D\, \partial d) = 0$$
$$\partial NPV/\partial X = (\partial h\, \partial q\, \partial Y/\partial q\, \partial Y\, \partial X) + (\partial h\, \partial I/\partial I\, \partial X) = 0 \tag{1-8}$$

The industry will maximize profits where (1) the marginal value of accelerating production equals the marginal investment costs of development (intensive margin) and (2) the marginal value of newly developed reserves equals the marginal investment costs of exploration (extensive margin).

In Equations (1-8), the critical values of X and d are clearly functions of the vector α of parametric constants. Solution of Equations (1-8) for $X = l(\alpha)$ and $d = m(\alpha)$ and substitution of these derived functions in Equations (1-1), (1-2), and (1-6) gives production in year t, q_t, as a function of α. This functional relationship, giving the quantity produced as a function of the product price α_1, represents the supply schedule. Different values of α_2, α_3, . . . , α_7 shift the supply schedule to either the right or the left.

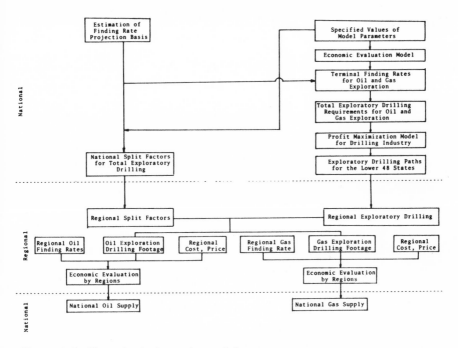

Figure 1-1. Flow chart of supply model.

Figure 1-1 shows how supply functions for crude oil and natural gas (non-associated) are generally estimated in our study. First, a national analysis is made to (1) estimate a finding rate projection basis, (2) determine terminal finding rates for oil and gas exploration, (3) calculate total exploratory drilling paths, and (4) split total exploratory drilling into that for oil and for gas. Second, a regional analysis is made to estimate regional finding rates, exploratory drilling footages, product prices, and costs. Estimates of supply functions for crude oil and natural gas in the lower 48 states are the respective sums of these regional estimates.

The models and the data for estimating the supply functions are developed in Chapters 2, 3, and 4. Economic supplies of crude oil and natural gas from new onshore reserves in the lower 48 states are estimated in Chapter 5. Estimates of total production from old reserves in the lower 48 states, as well as from offshore and Alaskan sources, are made in Chapter 6 to complete the analysis.

2

Economics of Petroleum Exploration, Development, and Production for New On-Shore Sources in the Lower 48 States

Profits are assumed to be the key force stimulating the petroleum industry to explore for new reserves and to produce oil and gas from those reserves. Profits are discounted to the present at a specified discount rate to have a comparable measure of net monetary returns and to take into account the value of the alternative opportunities foregone by investing in oil and gas exploration and production. Figure 2-1 illustrates the typical cash flow of an investment made in a petroleum exploratory venture. In a risky venture, heavy front-end investments must be made first followed by smaller investments. If successful, the net returns from this investment decline exponentially over the economic life of the newly found reserves.

In the analysis below, the time period from the start of a successful drilling project to the first production from that project (T_e) is assumed to be one year. The total front-end investment for exploration and development of the new reserve is assumed to be expended in the first year. This investment constitutes an initial negative cash flow for the project. With exponential production from the new reserve, the annual depletion rate is a constant fraction of the reserve remaining at the beginning of each year:

Year	Unexploited Reserve Remaining	Production
0	ΔY	—
1	$\Delta Y(1\text{-}d)$	ΔYd
2	$\Delta Y(1\text{-}d)^2$	$\Delta Y(1\text{-}d)d$
3	$\Delta Y(1\text{-}d)^3$	$\Delta Y(1\text{-}d)^2d$
.	.	.
.	.	.
.	.	.

Assuming constant petroleum prices over the economic life of the project, gross revenues from the venture will follow an exponential production path. Also, royalties to the mineral rights owners, severance taxes to the state,

6

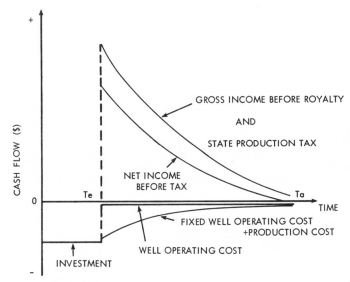

Figure 2-1. Cash flow of petroleum exploration, development, and production.

and production costs of the project will generally be proportional to gross revenues from oil and gas production. The economic life of the project will cease at time T_a, when the net revenue goes to zero.

The following sections describe the investment, revenue, production cost, and tax considerations of importance to the cash flow. Also, the method of evaluating secondary and tertiary oil recoveries, in addition to primary recovery, is discussed. Historical relationships for 1966-1974 are used to allocate the modeling results for the nation to the important production regions of the nation; see Figure 2-2 for a regional delineation.

2.1. Drilling Costs (Investment)

The total cost of drilling exploratory wells is the sum of the drilling cost for productive oil wells and those for dry holes. That is,

$$TEDC = PEDC + DEDC, \qquad (2-1)$$

where $TEDC$ = total exploratory drilling cost,
$PEDC$ = productive exploratory drilling cost, and
$DEDC$ = dry-hole exploratory drilling cost.

Further, productive and dry-hole costs can be expressed as:

$$DEDC = CDD \cdot DE \cdot \Delta X, \text{ and}$$
$$PEDC = CDO(1 - DE)\Delta X,$$

where CDD = average cost of drilling and equipping dry holes,

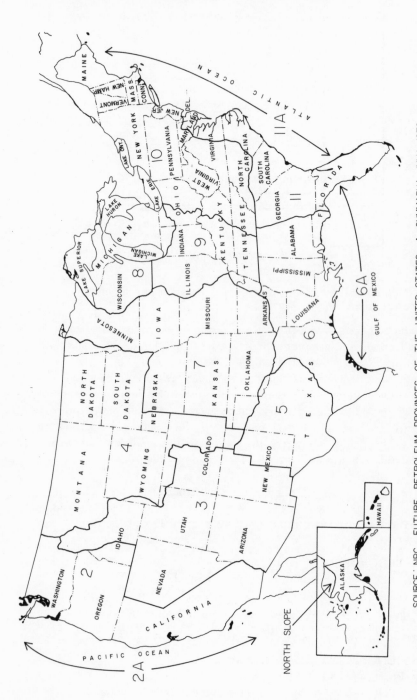

SOURCE: NPC, FUTURE PETROLEUM PROVINCES OF THE UNITED STATES, A SUMMARY; JULY 1970 – WITH SLIGHT MODIFICATION.

Figure 2-2. The NPC Oil Regions.

CDO = average cost of drilling and equipping productive oil wells,
DE = ratio of dry-hole footage to total exploratory footage drilled, and
ΔX = footage of new exploratory drilling.

Similar cost relationships hold for drilling and equipping gas wells, with CDO being replaced by CDG. National and regional data for drilling costs for CDO, CDG, and CDD are given in Tables 2-1, 2-2, and 2-3. Costs in 1974 dollars were used in the model.

Table 2-1. Average Oil Well Drilling and Equipment Cost (CDO) ($/ft)*

Year	Region								U.S. Avg.
	2	3	4	5	6	7	8, 9, 10	11	
1966	20.61	15.02	14.89	11.56	13.95	10.82	7.95	22.60	11.45
1967	18.23	19.74	15.50	12.28	15.34	10.26	9.62	22.65	13.04
1968	16.86	23.89	14.73	12.99	15.48	11.31	8.72	23.21	13.32
1969	21.72	17.30	13.77	13.04	15.97	11.81	8.56	24.12	13.61
1970	18.84	25.00	15.60	12.75	24.75	12.76	9.37	25.00	16.23
1971	20.43	27.78	15.19	14.10	18.46	12.93	10.47	25.80	15.60
1972	25.51	37.91	17.16	13.62	21.45	12.22	11.63	26.95	17.00
1973	27.14	50.03	21.29	15.20	22.20	15.71	14.47	30.57	19.62
1974	40.16	50.56	23.15	19.08	32.30	18.72	18.11	37.48	25.45

*Data source: API (1962–1975).

Table 2-2. Average Gas Well Drilling and Equipment Cost (CDG) ($/ft)*

Year	Region								U.S. Avg.
	2	3	4	5	6	7	8, 9, 10	11	
1966	18.83	12.43	18.44	26.82	26.22	13.61	9.82	27.38	17.45
1967	17.69	12.36	18.75	32.66	28.09	14.74	11.26	27.43	20.93
1968	20.36	14.75	29.11	35.57	25.33	15.61	10.73	28.12	20.83
1969	21.86	12.68	18.97	29.81	24.16	19.29	12.04	29.22	19.90
1970	17.11	12.64	24.01	42.34	27.82	24.59	12.66	30.29	23.42
1971	17.70	12.81	17.92	38.20	27.90	27.96	12.07	31.24	23.45
1972	25.72	18.88	18.64	38.42	29.41	25.49	13.70	32.67	24.61
1973	31.68	18.49	28.91	35.30	29.21	30.13	14.35	36.95	25.89
1947	32.71	24.40	24.28	52.61	45.75	36.77	19.95	43.92	32.80

*Data source: API (1962–1975).

Table 2-3. Average Dry Well Drilling Cost (CDD) ($/ft)*

Year	Region								U.S. Avg.
	2	3	4	5	6	7	8, 9, 10	11	
1966	10.09	11.14	8.11	9.20	10.77	8.06	6.34	17.01	8.64
1967	14.06	13.80	8.72	9.78	11.08	7.51	6.55	17.05	9.68
1968	12.02	15.72	9.91	10.77	12.62	8.55	6.53	17.47	10.70
1969	12.13	8.45	7.90	11.07	12.82	8.23	6.65	18.15	10.20
1970	13.04	10.23	8.64	13.10	15.10	9.07	8.66	18.82	11.76
1971	15.73	11.25	9.45	12.72	16.62	10.31	8.42	19.41	12.94
1972	17.03	13.43	9.29	12.65	16.86	10.25	9.81	20.30	13.01
1973	24.89	17.72	12.43	14.26	18.23	12.19	13.10	22.46	15.53
1974	23.03	21.31	12.75	16.55	21.10	14.89	13.52	27.29	21.79

*Data source: API (1962–1975).

Data for the dry-hole ratio (DE) are listed in Table 2-4. See the bottom line of Table 2-4 for the dry-hole ratio for oil and gas exploration used in the model.

Development drilling follows successful exploratory drilling. Historically, development drilling has been a fairly constant ratio of exporatory drilling. Total cost of development drilling is the sum of productive development drilling cost and dry-hole development drilling cost.

For oil development,

$$TDDC = PDDC + DDDC, \qquad (2-2)$$

where TDDC = total development drilling cost,

PDDC = productive development drilling cost, and

DDDC = dry-hole development drilling cost.

Productive and dry-hole costs are similar to exploratory drilling costs and can be expressed as follows:

$$PDDC = (TDRO - 1)(1 - DD)CDD \cdot \Delta X, \qquad (2-3)$$
$$DDDC = (TDRO - 1)DD \cdot CDD \cdot \Delta X,$$

where TDRO = ratio of total net drilling footage (exploratory plus development) to exploratory drilling footage, and

DD = ratio of dry-hole footage to total development footage drilled.

For gas development, substitute TDRG for TDRO ano CDG for CDO in (2-3). Data for DD, TDRO, and TDRG are given in Tables 2-5, 2-6, and 2-7.

The total drilling cost (TDC) for a project is the sum of productive drilling cost (PDC) and dry-hole drilling cost (DDC). That is,

$$TDC = PDC + DDC, \qquad (2-4)$$

where PDC = PEDC + PDDC, and
DDC = DEDC + DDDC.

Geological and geophysical exploration expenses (GGE) have averaged around 18% of TDC; see Table 2-8. The GGE expenses consist of the portion allocated to dry holes (GGED) and the portion allocated to productive wells (GGEP). Thus,

$$GGE = 0.18\ TDC, \qquad\qquad (2\text{-}5)$$
$$GGEP = GGE \cdot PDC/TDC, \text{ and}$$
$$GGED = GGE \cdot DDC/TDC.$$

Cost of primary lease equipment (PLEC) is assumed to be 20% of TDC, and cost of exploratory and development overhead (OVHD) is assumed to be 30% of these drilling costs:

$$PLEC = 0.2\ TDC \qquad\qquad (2\text{-}6)$$
$$OVHD = 0.3\ TDC$$

These costs are based on the historical averages listed in Tables 2-9 and 2-10.

Part of the investment made is expensed in the current year (EXPI); the remainder is depreciated over a 10-yr. period. Current expense items include:

—dry-hole drilling costs (DDC),

—dry-hole geological and geophysical costs (GGED),

—exploratory and development overhead (OVHD), and

—the intangible portion of productive well drilling and equipping costs. Intangible drilling costs make up 70% of productive oil well drilling and equipping cost and 73% of productive gas well drilling and equipping cost.

Table 2-4. Exploratory Drilling Footage Success Ratio by Regions (DE)*

	Region								U.S.
Year	2	3	4	5	6	7	8, 9, 10	11	Avg.†
1966	0.111	0.172	0.139	0.259	0.169	0.320	0.186	—	0.195
1967	0.152	0.144	0.159	0.246	0.185	0.248	0.186	—	0.208
1968	0.075	0.105	0.124	0.257	0.169	0.206	0.259	—	0.164
1969	0.097	0.149	0.132	0.281	0.208	0.247	0.247	0.124	0.201
1970	0.152	0.152	0.117	0.234	0.202	0.232	0.224	0.194	0.193
1971	0.120	0.131	0.113	0.246	0.172	0.198	0.226	—	0.174
1972	0.137	0.260	0.140	0.245	0.167	0.231	0.309	0.013	0.191
1973	0.151	0.174	0.141	0.330	0.210	0.253	0.350	0.090	0.224
1974	0.167	0.170	0.155	0.330	0.261	0.240	0.407	0.061	0.249
Values used in model	0.129	0.162	0.136	0.270	0.194	0.242	0.266	0.096	0.200

*Data source: Dillon and Van Dyke (1967), Van Dyke (1968), Van Dyke and Dix (1969), Dix (1970), Inglehart and Dix (1971), Inglehart (1972, 1973), Wagner and Inglehart (1974), and Wagner (1975).

(text continued on page 15)

Table 2-5. Development Drilling Footage Success Ratio by Regions (DD)*

Year	2	3	4	5	6	7	8, 9, 10	11	U.S. Avg.
1966	0.898	0.855	0.644	0.820	0.682	0.683	0.752	0.594	0.748
1967	0.892	0.843	0.690	0.806	0.665	0.688	0.778	—	0.734
1968	0.890	0.813	0.733	0.808	0.665	0.670	0.812	0.750	0.737
1969	0.856	0.808	0.696	0.803	0.671	0.696	0.814	1.000	0.738
1970	0.886	0.815	0.712	0.842	0.696	0.665	0.845	0.847	0.756
1971	0.900	0.820	0.697	0.850	0.709	0.674	0.833	1.000	0.765
1972	0.820	0.821	0.615	0.856	0.694	0.668	0.846	0.939	0.750
1973	0.830	0.926	0.730	0.848	0.684	0.660	0.861	0.746	0.767
1974	0.857	0.886	0.703	0.852	0.700	0.667	0.860	0.446	0.767
Values used in model	0.870	0.843	0.702	0.832	0.685	0.675	0.822	0.703	0.751

*Data source: See footnote to Table 2-4.

Table 2-6. Total Drilling Footage and Exploratory Drilling Footage Ratio (Oil) (TDRD)*

Year	2	3	4	5	6	7	8, 9, 10	11	U.S. Avg.
1966	5.129	1.776	2.015	4.412	3.283	5.479	4.498	1.417	4.020
1967	4.639	1.839	1.915	4.445	2.976	3.892	5.298	—	3.396
1968	4.596	1.919	1.853	4.729	2.755	3.631	6.172	—	3.218
1969	4.093	1.575	1.782	4.231	3.176	3.793	7.576	1.604	3.192
1970	4.685	1.560	1.950	5.263	3.187	4.155	8.556	2.084	3.507
1971	4.922	1.565	1.994	5.773	3.972	3.825	4.210	—	3.894
1972	4.923	1.931	1.902	6.283	4.188	3.994	4.993	1.429	3.639
1973	4.572	3.352	1.937	7.331	3.326	4.225	5.016	1.889	3.987
1974	4.877	3.920	1.995	6.157	3.188	4.398	5.103	1.584	4.026
Values used in model	4.715	2.160	1.927	5.403	3.339	4.155	5.714	1.668	3.653

*Data source: Dillon and Van Dyke (1967), Van Dyke (1968), Van Dyke and Dix (1969), Inglehart and Dix (1971), Inglehart (1972, 1973), Wagner and Inglehart (1974), and Wagner (1975).

Table 2-7. Total Drilling Footage and Exploratory Drilling Footage Ratio
(Gas) (TDRG)*

Year	\multicolumn{8}{c}{Region}	U.S. Avg.
	2	3	4	5	6	7	8, 9, 10	11	U.S. Avg.
1966	1.386	7.089	1.699	2.166	1.613	2.293	3.810	—	2.064
1967	1.464	6.805	1.715	2.384	1.615	2.915	4.339	1.000	2.091
1968	1.702	5.513	1.495	2.676	1.749	2.895	3.796	—	2.130
1969	1.910	3.826	1.429	2.172	1.530	2.790	4.492	—	1.969
1970	1.842	3.505	1.475	2.486	1.916	2.221	5.282	—	2.255
1971	2.286	2.688	1.577	3.003	1.845	2.374	6.871	—	2.508
1972	1.790	3.856	1.576	1.945	1.762	2.777	5.281	—	2.184
1973	1.526	4.193	1.616	2.162	1.879	2.705	5.081	—	2.330
1974	1.645	3.901	1.654	2.504	1.741	3.796	3.913	—	2.330
Values used in model	1.728	4.597	1.582	2.389	1.739	2.752	4.763	2.200†	2.207

*Data source: See footnote to Table 2-4.
†National average; value is assumed because of lack of historical data.

Table 2-8. Geological and Geophysical Expenses (GGE)*

Year	Total Well Drilling and Equipping Cost ($MM)	Geological and Geophysical Expenses ($MM)	Ratio
1960	2,425	381	0.157
1961	2,398	395	0.165
1962	2,576	407	0.158
1963	2,302	417	0.181
1964	2,428	436	0.180
1965	2,402	457	0.190
1966	2,360	448	0.190
1967	2,299	478	0.209
1968	2,409	455	0.189
1969	2,611	480	0.184
1970	2,578	447	0.173
1971	2,372	461	0.194
1972	2,814	477	0.170
1973	3,075	531	0.173
1974	—	—	—
1975	—	—	—
Value used in model	—	—	0.180

*Data source: API (1962–1975).

Table 2-9. Primary Lease Equipment Cost (PLEC)*

Year	Total Well Drilling and Equipping Cost ($MM)	Primary Lease Equipment Cost ($MM)	Ratio
1960	2,425	431	0.178
1961	2,398	446	0.186
1962	2,576	497	0.193
1963	2,302	447	0.194
1964	2,428	504	0.208
1965	2,402	430	0.179
1966	2,360	459	0.194
1967	2,299	428	0.186
1968	2,409	384	0.159
1969	2,611	442	0.169
1970	2,578	443	0.172
1971	2,372	388	0.164
1972	2,814	497	0.177
1973	3,075	524	0.170
1974	—	—	—
1975	—	—	—
Value used in model	—	—	0.200

*Data source: API (1962–1975).

Table 2-10. Overhead Expenses for Exploration and Development (OVHD)*

Year	Total Well Drilling and Equipping Cost ($MM)	Overhead ($MM)	Ratio
1960	2,425	507	0.209
1961	2,398	538	0.224
1962	2,576	550	0.214
1963	2,302	544	0.236
1964	2,428	577	0.238
1965	2,402	560	0.233
1966	2,360	671	0.284
1967	2,299	704	0.306
1968	2,409	727	0.302
1969	2,611	765	0.293
1970	2,578	722	0.280
1971	2,372	735	0.310
1972	2,814	803	0.285
1973	3,075	913	0.297
1974	—	—	—
1975	—	—	—
Value used in model	—	—	0.300

*Data source: API (1962–1975).

Capitalized expenditures (CAPI) include:
—tangible cost of drilling productive wells,
—productive geological and geophysical costs (GGEP), and
—primary lease equipment costs (PLEC).

Investment tax credits may be obtained from capitalized expenditures at the tax credit rate and expressed as:

$$TC = t_c \cdot CAPI, \tag{2-7}$$

where TC = investment tax credits,
t_c = tax credit rate (%), and
CAPI = capital expenditures.

2.2.   Investment Variations for Different Production Rates

The Industry may deplete a new increment of reserves (ΔY) at different production rates, which are commonly called depletion rates. Different depletion rates (d) will affect only the investment for development. That is, more development drilling is required if the depletion rate selected for the new increment of reserves is greater than the historical rate (d^o); similarly, less development drilling is required if the depletion rate is less than d^o. Table 2-11 shows average historical rates of oil and gas depletion rates for each of the regions.

Figure 2-3 illustrates how adjustments need to be made in development drilling footages for depletion rates both above and below historical experience. The development drilling required to increase the depletion rate (d) above the historical depletion rate (d^o) increases exponentially and is greater for large than for small historical depletion rates. Figure 2-3 illustrates an opposite relationship holds true for a depletion rate less than historical experience.

In our study, MacAvoy and Pindyck's investment equation for development drilling (1973) was used to estimate consistent values for the investment in development drilling ($\lambda \Delta D$), the ratio of total oil drilling to exploratory drilling footage (TDRO), and the depletion rate (d). MacAvoy and Pindyck's equation is:

$$I = A + C \cdot q \cdot \exp(Bd), \tag{2-8}$$

where A = start-up cost,
q = production capacity from new incremental reserves,
d = depletion rate, and
C & B = parametric constants.

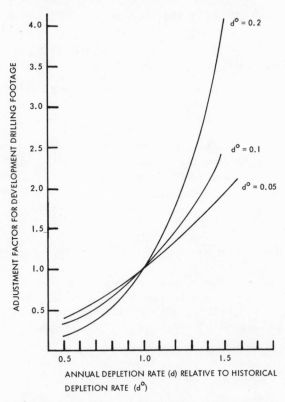

Figure 2-3. Adjustment factor has function of d/d^o.

Table 2-11. Annual Oil Depletion Rate and Annual Gas Depletion Rate*

Region	d^o (Oil)	d^o (Gas)
2	0.085	0.090
3	0.122	0.144
4	0.138	0.130
5	0.107	0.072
6	0.111	0.091
7	0.144	0.090
8, 9, 10	0.136	0.177
11	0.156	0.120

*Data source: FEA (1974).

The expression $C \cdot q \cdot e^{Bd}$ yields the increasing development drilling costs resulting from "well interference." Well interference results when the production of each new well decreases the production of existing wells in a field by a certain percentage. MacAvoy and Pindyck estimated B to be 10. If we neglect the start-up cost A, the investment adjustment factor becomes

$$(d/d^o) \exp [B(d - d^o)]. \qquad (2\text{-}9)$$

2.3. Revenue

The annual revenue stream to producers is the product of the annual production flow (Equation 1-6) and the prices of the products. This also includes consideration of associated natural gas in the case of crude oil production and natural gas liquids in the case of natural gas production. Historically, these by-products have been fairly constant percentages of the primary product; see Table 2-12 for a regional summary of associated gas production per barrel of crude oil (GOR), and natural gas liquid production per 1000 cubic feet (Mcf) of non-associated natural gas production (OGR). The price of natural gas liquids averaged 69.7% of the crude oil price in the nation from 1965-1974.

Petroleum prices have varied considerably from one region to another; however, the ratios of these prices to the national average price have been fairly constant (see Tables 2-13 and 2-14 for normalized oil and gas prices for 1965-1973). These historical ratios are assumed in our study to continue in the future.

Gross revenues (G) from the sale of crude oil (G_o) and non-associated natural gas (G_g) are expressed in the following way:

$$G_o = (P_o + P_g \cdot GOR) q_o, \qquad (2\text{-}10)$$
$$G_g = (P_g + 0.697 P_o \cdot OGR) q_g,$$

where P_o = crude oil price ($/bbl),

P_g = natural gas price ($/Mcf), and the ratio of natural gas liquids price to crude oil price is 0.697.

The royalty rate (R) for onshore production is 12.5% of gross revenue. State production taxes are summarized in Table 2-15 for each region.

Net revenue (NR) to the operator after paying royalty and state production taxes is:

$$NR = G(1 - R - AST), \qquad (2\text{-}11)$$

where AST is average state production taxes.

Table 2-12. Regional Summary of Associated Gas Production (GOR) per Barrel of Crude Oil and Natural Gas Liquid Production (OGR) per Mcf Natural Gas*

Region	GOR	OGR
2	0.442	0.041
3	0.828	0.026
4	0.855	0.026
5	0.947	0.050
6	1.466	0.033
7	1.369	0.031
8, 9, 10	0.688	0.0133
11	0.520	0.033

*Data source: FEA (1974).

Table 2-13. Normalized Wellhead Crude Oil Price by Regions*

	Region							
Year	2	3	4	5	6	7	8, 9, 10	11
1965	0.830	0.954	0.884	1.007	1.074	1.003	1.058	—
1966	0.816	0.953	0.896	1.004	1.072	1.008	1.079	—
1967	0.793	0.939	0.896	1.009	1.067	1.007	1.087	—
1968	0.799	0.942	0.904	1.013	1.066	1.014	1.086	—
1969	0.794	0.940	0.911	1.020	1.062	1.015	1.068	—
1970	0.801	0.925	0.927	1.015	1.060	1.009	1.055	—
1971	0.805	0.935	0.928	1.013	1.059	1.015	1.059	—
1972	0.801	0.937	0.930	1.012	1.059	1.014	1.062	—
1973	0.795	0.986	0.974	1.014	1.041	1.010	1.134	1.174
Values used in model	0.804	0.946	0.980†	1.012	1.062	1.011	1.150†	1.174

*Data source: Mineral Yearbook, U.S. Department of the Interior (1947–1975). Regional price divided by national average price is the normalized price.
†Values based on trend; others are averages.

2.4. Production Expenses

Total well operating cost (WOC) is the product of operating cost per well and the total number of productive wells (exploratory and development); see Table 2-16 for a regional summary of average well operating costs. The number of productive exploratory wells (NPEW) is calculated by dividing the successful exploratory drilling footage ($(1 - DE)\Delta X$) by the average depth of successful exploratory wells. The number of producing development wells (NPDW) is calculated similarly. See Tables 2-17 and 2-18 for average regional depths of productive exploratory oil and gas wells from 1966-1974; also, see Tables 2-19 and 2-20 for average regional depths of productive development oil and gas wells from 1966-1974.

Table 2-14. Normalized Wellhead Natural Gas Price by Region*

Year	Region							
	2	3	4	5	6	7	8, 9, 10	11
1965	2.015	0.802	0.864	0.827	1.017	0.893	1.575	0.841
1966	1.992	0.817	0.897	0.829	1.016	0.893	1.581	0.913
1967	1.885	0.834	0.899	0.835	1.025	0.890	1.577	0.939
1968	1.918	0.872	0.891	0.837	1.020	0.879	1.613	0.919
1969	1.869	0.881	0.879	0.837	1.023	0.908	1.619	0.959
1970	1.916	0.874	0.862	0.858	1.019	0.902	1.546	—
1971	1.930	0.924	0.902	0.907	1.086	0.932	1.618	1.771
1972	2.006	0.960	0.874	0.918	1.013	0.859	1.699	1.744
1973	1.787	0.998	0.896	0.960	1.000	0.852	1.730	1.643
Values used in model	1.924	1.000†	0.885	0.980†	1.024	0.890	1.618	1.700†

*Data source: Mineral Yearbook, U.S. Department of the Interior (1947–1975). Regional price divided by national average price is normalized price.
†Values based on trend; others are averages.

Table 2-15. Ad Valorem and State Production Tax*

Region	Oil Tax Rate	Gas Tax Rate
2	.08	.08
3	.0	.0
4	.07138	.07038
5	.08275	.07914
6	.08178	.10545
7	.097651	.13769
8, 9, 10	.0	.0
11	.07104	.08245

*Data source: FEA (1974).

The indirect overhead expenses assigned to production are treated as a fixed percentage of the gross revenue (G). This overhead expense ran about 3% of the gross revenue since 1960; see Table 2-21.

The production expense (PE) is the sum of the well operating cost and indirect overhead expense assigned to production:

$$PE = WOC + 0.03\,G \qquad (2\text{-}12)$$

If gross revenue does not cover production expenses, royalties, and state production taxes, the production terminates.

Table 2-16. Average Well Operating Cost ($/yr/well)*

Region	Oil Wells	Gas Wells
2	6,178	4,500
3	19,454	6,375
4	6,178	7,625
5	4,388	12,062
6	6,178	12,200
7	4,388	5,625
8, 9, 10	1,121	1,250
11	19,454	7,625

*Data source: FEA (1974).

Table 2-17. Average Depth of Exploratory Oil Wells by Regions (ft)*

	Region								U.S.
Year	2	3	4	5	6	7	8, 9, 10	11	Avg.
1966	6,878	5,857	6,467	6,422	8,121	4,818	2,064	5,838	5,335
1967	4,879	5,079	5,857	6,483	8,146	4,382	2,109	—	5,459
1968	5,385	5,901	7,004	6,061	8,607	4,743	2,293	—	5,729
1969	6,718	6,212	7,261	6,207	2,945	4,769	2,167	5,994	4,512
1970	6,115	7,716	7,716	5,866	3,364	4,813	2,332	15,847	4,655
1971	4,958	7,604	7,271	5,860	8,632	4,478	2,655	—	5,558
1972	5,430	7,870	6,832	5,628	8,835	5,113	3,123	15,903	5,903
1973	6,075	7,399	7,839	5,598	3,223	4,687	3,315	10,815	4,549
1974	5,436	4,848	7,624	5,862	8,492	5,350	3,339	11,641	5,892
Values used in model	5,800	6,500	7,100	6,000	6,800	4,800	3,300	13,600	5,288

*Data source: See footnote to Table 2-4.

Table 2-18. Average Depth of Exploratory Gas Wells by Regions (ft)*

	Region								U.S.
Year	2	3	4	5	6	7	8, 9, 10	11	Avg.
1966	8,651	6,080	5,942	7,965	10,238	15,277	3,867	—	8,841
1967	6,879	5,763	3,853	8,772	9,800	5,824	2,837	—	7,071
1968	7,006	8,270	4,585	9,506	9,755	7,558	3,517	—	7,256
1969	5,830	5,702	5,930	9,956	5,023	7,342	3,921	—	5,493
1970	6,759	4,422	4,270	9,316	4,668	8,058	3,872	—	5,289
1971	6,270	6,159	5,443	6,865	9,365	8,397	3,178	—	7,220
1972	6,571	7,234	4,523	8,919	10,120	8,825	3,777	—	7,601
1973	5,917	2,263	4,797	6,349	3,589	7,342	4,226	—	4,497
1974	5,070	6,988	5,152	7,124	7,755	5,979	4,015	—	6,276
Values used in model	5,600	5,900	5,000	8,400	7,900	7,500	4,100†	14,000‡	6,616

*Data source: See footnote to Table 2-4.
†Values based on trend, others are averages.
‡FEA (1974).

Table 2-19. Average Depth of Development Oil Wells by Regions (ft)*

Year	Region 2	3	4	5	6	7	8, 9, 10	11	U.S. Avg.
1966	2,198	5,041	4,663	4,321	4,853	3,738	1,796	8,647	3,652
1967	1,876	3,832	4,611	3,972	4,915	3,703	2,200	8,650	3,762
1968	1,975	4,447	5,543	4,509	5,396	3,683	2,287	8,681	3,747
1969	2,351	4,426	5,960	4,654	4,711	3,924	2,210	9,729	3,907
1970	2,297	4,560	7,062	4,526	5,539	3,687	2,179	12,479	4,012
1971	2,102	5,475	5,569	4,667	5,013	3,440	2,047	12,179	3,815
1972	2,238	6,575	5,749	4,562	5,319	3,772	2,111	15,247	4,053
1973	2,347	8,415	5,462	4,752	5,416	3,765	2,208	14,550	4,175
1974	1,891	7,552	5,823	4,265	4,714	3,721	1,750	12,352	3,501
Values used in model	3,200	8,000†	6,000†	4,500	5,100	3,800	2,100	13,000	3,847

*Data source: See footnote to Table 2-4.
† Values based on trend; others are averages.

Table 2-20. Average Depth of Development Gas Wells by Regions (ft)*

Year	Region 2	3	4	5	6	7	8, 9, 10	11	U.S. Avg.
1966	6,214	5,307	5,608	6,818	7,602	6,140	3,022	—	5,288
1967	6,591	5,427	5,080	7,622	7,086	6,153	3,057	—	5,737
1968	5,944	5,828	4,419	7,909	7,697	6,419	3,198	—	5,404
1969	6,412	4,695	5,094	7,705	7,549	6,053	3,438	—	5,188
1970	5,510	4,953	3,927	8,843	7,833	5,408	3,795	—	5,303
1971	5,488	5,478	6,587	9,194	7,103	4,934	3,572	—	5,276
1972	5,290	4,718	3,746	7,427	6,225	5,483	3,576	—	4,924
1973	6,067	4,300	4,416	7,455	7,100	4,262	3,671	—	4,718
1974	5,170	5,169	4,571	7,321	5,880	5,423	3,589	—	5,035
Values used in model	5,900	5,200	4,900	7,900	7,200	5,600	3,500	11,400	5,208

*Data source: See footnote to Table 2-4. Dillon (1967), Van Dyke (1968, 1969), Dix (1970), Inglehart (1971, 1972, 1973), and Wagner (1974, 1975).

2.5. Net Present Value Determination

The net cash flow (NCF) to the operator from an increment of new eserves equals net revenue less investments, operating expense, and corporate income taxes. Net revenue equals gross revenue reduced by royalties nd state production taxes, and investments include those amortized over specific depreciation period as well as those deducted as current expenses.

Thus,

$$NCF = NR - CAPI - EXPI \qquad (2\text{-}13)$$
$$- [t(NR - DP - DA - PE - EXPI) - TC],$$

where NR = net revenue,
$\quad CAPI$ = capitalized expenditures,
$\quad EXPI$ = investment expensed in the current year,
$\quad t$ = corporate tax rate,
$\quad DP$ = depreciation allowance,
$\quad DA$ = depletion allowance,
$\quad PE$ = production expense, and
$\quad TC$ = investment tax credit.

Intangible drilling costs and dry-hole drilling expenses may either be deducted as current expenses or amortized over a specified depreciation period, depending on the policy assumptions below.

With given values for the depletion rate (d) and exploratory drilling (X), the gross revenues for the project are determined. Specification of the remaining parameters in Equations (2-11), (2-12), and (2-13) determines the net cash flow from the project.

The net present value (NPV) is calculated by mid-year discounting methods for the NCF from the project throughout its economic life of T_a years:

$$NPV = \sum_{i=1}^{T_a} \frac{NCF(i)}{(1+r)^{i-0.5}} \qquad (2\text{-}14)$$

where r is the specified discount rate for the project. Appendix I summarizes mathematical equations used to calculate the NPV.

2.6. Secondary and Tertiary Recoveries of New Oil

For crude oil, secondary and tertiary recoveries are possible in addition to primary recoveries. Primary recoveries are crude oil productions which result from internal pressures existing within the oil deposit. Once discovered, the oil flows naturally to the surface without any additional moving force. Secondary recovery begins when flow rates from primary recovery become economically inadequate and involves more expensive flow maintenance techniques such as pumping and water injection into the reservoir. Tertiary recovery usually follows secondary recovery and resorts to even more expensive techniques such as steam injection and the use of certain chemicals to improve the flow characteristics of the remaining crude in the reservoir.

Table 2-21. Overhead Expenses for Production*

Year	Gross Revenue ($MM)	Production Overhead ($MM)	Ratio
1960	9,211	271	0.0294
1961	9,562	292	0.0305
1962	9,919	306	0.0308
1963	10,294	301	0.0292
1964	10,405	295	0.0284
1965	10,653	312	0.0293
1966	11,429	306	0.0268
1967	12,274	317	0.0258
1968	12,964	340	0.0262
1969	13,882	369	0.0266
1970	14,919	416	0.0279
1971	15,789	465	0.0295
1972	15,893	467	0.0294
1973	17,952	485	0.0270
Value used in model	—	—	0.0300

*Data source: API (1962–1975).

In our study, the economic viability of new oil exploration was evaluated considering all three types of recovery techniques. That is, if primary recovery was deemed profitable but secondary and tertiary recoveries were not, then only primary recovery was undertaken. However, if primary recovery was not deemed profitable but the combination of primary, secondary, and tertiary recoveries was, then oil exploration was undertaken.

Evaluation of enhanced recoveries involves determination of (1) total new reserve additions from enhanced recovery methods, and (2) the cost (both operating and investment) of producing additional oil from these enhanced recovery reserve additions. To accomplish this evaluation, the secondary and tertiary recovery factors of FEA (1974) were used. These recovery factors are based on estimates of original oil-in-place (OIP), i.e., the estimate of the total crude oil contents of a reservoir whether or not the contents are recoverable. Thus, there exists an implied recovery factor for primary, secondary, and tertiary recovery such that estimated (recoverable) reserves are calculated as:

Total Recoverable Reserves = OIP (PRF + SRF + TRF),
where PRF = primary recovery factor,
SRF = secondary recovery factor, and
TRF = tertiary recovery factor.

Therefore, to use FEA's estimates of secondary and tertiary recovery factors, it was necessary to estimate OIP.

In our study, new oil discoveries are based on estimates of reserve additions rather than OIP. Historically, most reserve additions were from primary recovery; however, reserve additions from secondary and tertiary recoveries were also included in the historical reserve estimates. Because the historical reserve estimates include primary, secondary, and tertiary recovery, the reserve statistics can not be partitioned into contributions of different recovery techniques. Here, the original OIP is estimated in the following way. Currently, the average recovery factor for all conventional recovery techniques is approximately 30% of OIP. The PRFs used by the FEA for each region are summarized in Table 2-22. Regional crude oil reserve additions for 1966-1974 are summarized in Table 3-3. The PRF by the size of the reserve additions is a weighted average of 29%. This means FEA's PRF includes recoveries not only by primary recovery techniques but enhanced recovery techniques used in the past. In this case, OIP can be estimated as:

$$OIP = \Delta Y / PRF, \qquad (2\text{-}15)$$

where PRF is the primary recovery factor used by FEA. Additional reserves from secondary and tertiary recovery estimated by FEA represent the contributions of previously untried recovery methods. Additional reserves resulting from new secondary recovery techniques (ΔY_s) and new tertiary recovery techniques (ΔY_t) are given by:

$$\Delta Y_s = SRF(\Delta Y / PRF)$$
$$\Delta Y_t = TRF(\Delta Y / PRF) \qquad (2\text{-}16)$$

Table 2-22. Primary, Secondary, and Tertiary Recovery Factors for Crude Oil*

		Secondary		Tertiary	
Region	Primary	10 Years	15 Years	10 Years	15 Years
2	0.233	0.133	0.081	0.0405	0.0515
3	0.220	0.073	0.073	0.0	0.0
4	0.240	0.069	0.0586	0.015	0.0351
5	0.200	0.10	0.045	0.075	0.0675
6	0.465	0.015	0.0045	0.0045	0.00225
7	0.250	0.170	0.06	0.04	0.06
8, 9, 10	0.274	0.0845	0.0557	0.00427	0.0198
11	0.330	0.033	0.0	0.0	0.0

*Data source: FEA (1974).

Table 2-23. Investments and Production Costs ($/bbl) for Secondary and Tertiary Recovery*

Region	Secondary Recovery		Tertiary Recovery	
	Investment	Production Cost	Investment	Production Cost
2	0.32	1.143	1.5	1.5
3	0.32	0.5	0.8	5.5
4	0.32	0.5	0.8	5.5
5	0.32	0.5	0.8	5.5
6	0.32	0.5	0.8	5.5
7	0.32	0.5	0.8	5.5
8, 9, 10	0.32	0.5	0.8	5.5
11	0.32	0.5	0.8	5.5

*Data source: (1) Private communication, FEA data used in 1976 National Energy Outlook; (2) 1975 cost estimates were deflated by the wholesale price index (a factor of 1.1) to express in 1974 dollars.

In estimating the recovery factors, FEA made an assumption regarding the period over which primary recovery techniques would be effective and reported recovery factors for two different assumed time lags: 10 and 15 years. See Table 2-22 for a regional summary of primary and enhanced recovery factors for 10- and 15-year lags.

The FEA estimated the investment required ($/bbl) to add new reserves from secondary recovery (SRI) and tertiary recovery methods (TRI); see Table 2-23. The total investment required for secondary recovery (I_s) and tertiary recovery (I_t) is:

$$I_s = SRI \cdot \Delta Y_s \qquad (2\text{-}17)$$
$$I_t = TRI \cdot \Delta Y_t$$

Our study assumed investments I_s and I_t are made at the beginning of the enhanced recovery project with appropriate lagged time from the start of primary production from new discoveries. Depletion rates for enhanced recovery were assumed to be the same as for primary recovery. Production out of additional reserves (ΔY_s, ΔY_t) continues as long as the net revenues are greater than zero; see Table 2-23 for production cost per barrel of enhanced oil recovery as estimated by FEA (1976).

Cash flows from enhanced recoveries were discounted back to the present. Only enhanced recovery projects with a positive NPV were assumed to be undertaken. The positive NPV from enhanced recovery was added to that from primary recovery to evaluate the overall profitability of an exploratory drilling venture for crude oil.

Long-Term Trend of Petroleum Finding Rate

3

With the economic conditions specified (parametric constants), the finding rate for new petroleum reserves is the key to the economic viability of an exploratory drilling venture and future petroleum supply. Estimates of future finding rates are based on historical reserve estimates for oil and gas reported by the American Petroleum Institute (API, 1975).

The USGS estimates are based on geological evaluations of unexplored prospects by regional geologists. The USGS estimated the total volume of reserves from future discoveries. However, estimates of exploratory drilling footages required to produce these reserves are generally not provided. Also, the USGS do not give the implicitly assumed economic reference conditions. The API estimates ultimate reserves by year of discovery. Hubbert's revision factors (1974) were applied to the API data to estimate the growth in reserve estimates as fields grow old. Our study used API estimates as of December 1974.

Section 3.1 describes (1) how reserve estimates grow over time and (2) the role of exploratory and development drilling in revising these reserve estimates. The relation between drilling, reserve growth, and the USGS reserve estimates are explained. Historical finding rates are estimated in Section 3.2 from 1945-1974 data. Reserve estimates in our study are compared to USGS estimates in Chapter 5 (Miller et al., 1975).

3.1. Reserve Growth, Drilling, and Future Reserve Estimates

Figure 3-1 shows how exploratory drilling is divided into new field wildcats, new pool tests, and outpost extension test footages. The ultimate size of new discoveries is seldom known in the year of discovery. Initial estimates of new reserves are often small in relation to the total reserves resulting from a new discovery (API, 1970). The estimates of proven reserves are adjusted by revisions and extensions as described below.

Extensions of reserves are assigned to a reservoir as its proven area enlarges. This extension in reserves is found from exploratory drilling classified as outpost extension tests.

Revisions are changes in earlier estimates, either upward or downward, based on new engineering and/or geological information. Production history and development drilling provide additional data to improve estimates of proven reserves. Some exploratory drilling in new pool tests contributes to a revision of proven reserves. If new pool tests are significantly different from existing reservoirs, the new pool is classified as a new discovery. Revisions also include increases in proven reserves because of successful use of improved recovery techniques.

The growth in reserve estimates is closely tied to the estimates of reserves made by USGS. The USGS estimates of reserves are classified as "measured," "indicated," "inferred," and "undiscovered" reserves. The first three classifications are the reserves in identified fields. The undiscovered reserves are estimated to exist in favorable geological settings. Measured and indicated reserves are either already proven reserves or will become economically available by application of improved recovery techniques. These reserves are therefore, not affected by future drilling. Inferred reserves are the reserves that would eventually be added to known fields through extensions and revisions. Undiscovered reserves result from new field wildcat drilling footages and a portion of the new pool test drilling footages.

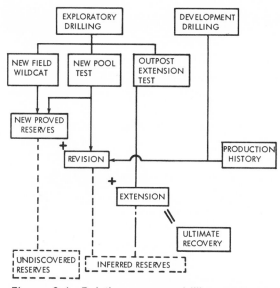

Figure 3-1. Relation among drilling, reserves, and growth of reserves.

Inferred reserves will be found from outpost extension tests and from part of the new pool tests; additional engineering and geological information from development drilling also contributes to these reserves. Historical data for 1946-1974 reported by the API (1975) indicate nearly equal growth in reserves from revisions and extensions for crude oil. This study assumes 50% of the reserve revisions result from new pool tests (classified as exploratory drilling) and 50% of the revisions result from more engineering and geological information. This means that future exploratory drilling will find undiscovered reserves and 75% of inferred reserves. Unlike crude oil, all inferred reserves and undiscovered reserves of natural gas will be found by future explorations.

3.2.   Long-Term Finding Rates of Oil and Gas

This section shows how the long-term finding rates of oil and gas for new exploratory drilling were estimated. The API estimates of ultimate recovery by year of discovery represent the total quantity of oil or gas that could be eventually produced from reservoirs discovered in a given year. These ultimate recovery estimates increase over time because of revisions and extensions.

Hubbert's equations (1974) for these growth curves have the following forms:

$$\Delta Y_\infty = \Delta Y_\tau \cdot \varepsilon, \tag{3-1}$$

where $\Delta Y_\infty =$ the estimated ultimate production of oil (or gas),

$\Delta Y_\tau =$ the current estimate of ultimate recovery, and

$\tau =$ the elapsed time from the year of discovery to the year when the estimates are made.

The Hubbert correction factor for oil is expressed as:

$$\varepsilon_0 = 1/[1 - \exp[-0.076(\tau + 1.503)]] \tag{3-2}$$

The Hubbert correction factor for gas is expressed as:

$$\varepsilon_g = 1/[1 - \exp[-0.063(\tau + 4.343)]] \tag{3-3}$$

Both Equations (3-2) and (3-3) show that the possible future growth in ultimate recovery decreases as the field ages. Table 3-1 summarizes the ultimate crude oil recovery by the year of discovery for 1945-1974, as corrected by Hubbert's equations. Similar information is given in Table 3-2 for natural gas.

Table 3-1. Exploratory Oil Well Drilling Footage and Ultimate Oil Recovery by Year of Discovery (Lower 48 States)

Year	Ultimate Oil Recovery (10⁶ bbl)*	Exploratory Oil Well Drilling Footage (10⁶ ft)†	Cumulative Ultimate Oil Recovery (10⁶ bbl)	Cumulative Exploratory Oil Well Drilling Footage (10⁶ ft)
1945	2,367.2	15.653	2,367.2	15.653
1946	1,638.8	14.599	4,006.0	30.252
1947	1,564.5	18.296	5,570.5	48.548
1948	3,893.3	22.244	9,463.8	70.792
1949	2,979.7	24.769	12,443.5	95.561
1950	2,377.1	29.906	14,820.6	125.467
1951	1,906.8	38.168	16,727.4	163.635
1952	1,490.6	39.410	18,218.0	203.045
1953	2,486.9	42.536	20,704.9	245.581
1954	1,628.8	40.206	22,333.7	285.787
1955	1,501.0	45.945	23,834.7	331.732
1956	1,524.9	49.691	25,359.6	381.423
1957	2,143.9	41.826	27,503.5	423.249
1958	1,318.1	37.020	28,821.6	460.269
1959	863.1	36.143	29,684.7	496.412
1960	1,210.0	30.169	30,894.7	526.581
1961	662.6	28.103	31,557.4	554.684
1962	758.1	28.180	32,315.5	582.864
1963	564.4	30.516	32,879.9	613.380
1964	873.1	32.417	33,753.0	645.797
1965	891.0	27.080	34,644.0	672.877
1966	727.0	28.208	35,371.0	701.085
1967	944.0	26.524	36,315.0	727.609
1968	840.0	27.779	37,155.0	755.388
1969	758.3	30.991	37,913.3	786.379
1970	1,648.9	24.570	39,562.2	810.949
1971	498.0	19.472	40,060.2	830.421
1972	547.5	19.767	40,607.7	850.188
1973	716.6	16.209	41,324.3	866.397
1974	324.3	18.520	41,648.6	884.917

*Data source: API (1975), adjusted by Hubbert (1974) revision factors.
†Data source: See footnote to Table 2-4.

Table 3-2. Exploratory Gas Well Drilling Footage and Ultimate Non-Associated
Gas Recovery by Year of Discovery
(Lower 48 States)

Year	Ultimate Gas Recovery (10⁹ scf)*	Exploratory Gas Well Drilling Footage (10⁶ ft)†	Cumulative Ultimate Gas Recovery (10⁹ scf)	Cumulative Exploratory Gas Well Drilling Footage (10⁶ ft)
1945	9,456.4	7.396	9,456.4	7.396
1946	4,804.1	7.740	14,260.5	15.136
1947	10,557.9	8.097	24,818.4	23.233
1948	5,373.4	10.507	30,191.8	33.740
1949	14,494.7	10.288	44,686.5	44.028
1950	9,744.4	10.269	54,430.9	54.297
1951	10,501.4	11.176	64,932.3	65.473
1952	17,137.2	15.755	82,069.5	81.228
1953	12,082.4	17.824	94,151.9	99.052
1954	11,894.8	18.799	106,046.7	117.851
1955	6,747.3	22.223	112,794.0	140.074
1956	13,741.6	23.159	126,535.6	163.233
1957	11,660.6	25.484	138,196.2	188.717
1958	12,789.5	23.254	150,985.7	211.971
1959	8,507.6	25.514	159,493.3	237.485
1960	10,578.6	24.151	170,071.9	261.636
1961	7,356.1	25.002	177,429.0	286.638
1962	7,287.4	23.555	184,716.4	310.193
1963	13,516.6	20.141	198,233.0	330.334
1964	5,874.7	20.294	204,107.7	350.628
1965	8,329.0	18.958	212,436.7	369.586
1966	8,390.0	23.417	220,826.8	393.003
1967	6,264.4	18.739	227,091.2	411.742
1968	7,833.1	18.304	234,924.3	430.046
1969	8,595.4	23.542	243,519.7	453.588
1970	5,950.8	17.865	249,470.5	471.453
1971	4,589.5	17.474	254,060.0	488.927
1972	7,664.7	22.699	261,724.7	511.626
1973	7,501.7	25.957	269,226.4	537.583
1974	4,896.0	29.283	274,122.4	566.866

*Data source: API (1975), adjusted by Hubbert (1974) revision factors.
†Data source: See footnote to Table 2-4.

Tables 3-1 and 3-2 also include exploratory drilling footages for oil and gas wells. About 80% of total exploratory drilling footages (new field wildcat, new pool test, and outpost extension test) is dry. In our study, the ratio of the successful exploratory drilling footage for oil to total successful exploratory drilling footage for oil and gas was the basic factor used to allocate the dry-hole drilling footage to oil. Similarly, the ratio of successful exploratory drilling footage for gas (non-associated) to total successful exploratory drilling footage for oil and gas was used as the basic factor to allocate dry-hole drilling footage to gas.

Figure 3-2 shows how cumulative increases in exploratory drilling footages for crude oil have resulted in cumulative increases in ultimate reserves of crude oil from 1945-1975. Increments of exploratory drilling footages have continually added more ultimate reserves at a decreasing rate to give a diminishing finding rate for crude oil. The following functional form was selected to give monotonically increasing cumulative finds with increased cumulative drilling, yet give a monotonically decreasing finding rate:

$$(\log F_o - b_o)^2 = b_1 + b_2 \log X_o, \qquad (3\text{-}4)$$

where F_o = the cumulative discoveries of crude oil reserve findings in millions of barrels, and

X_o = the cumulative exploratory drilling footage for oil in millions of feet since January 1945.

For crude oil, the regression estimate of Equation (3-4) for $b_o = 6.488$ is:

$$(\log F_o - 6.488)^2 = -9.7699 + 3.9343 \log X_o \qquad (3\text{-}5)$$
$$(-32.60) \quad (77.37)$$
$$R^2 = 0.9952 \quad DW = 1.149$$

The t-statistics for the regression coefficients (in parentheses below the respective coefficients) are highly significant. The value of b_o was selected to minimize the indicated serial correlation. Equation (3-5) is shown as the solid line in Figure 3-2.

Figure 3-3 shows how cumulative increases in exploratory drilling footages for natural gas (non-associated) have cumulatively increased ultimate reserves for natural gas from 1945-1975. Again, increments in exploratory drilling footages have continually added more ultimate reserves at a decreasing rate. The solid line is a plot of the following regression estimate of non-associated gas for $b_o = 6.365$:

$$(\log F_g - 6.365)^2 = -8.6262 + 7.3544 \log X_g \qquad (3\text{-}6)$$
$$(-18.20) \quad (81.13)$$
$$R^2 = 0.9956 \quad DW = 1.424$$

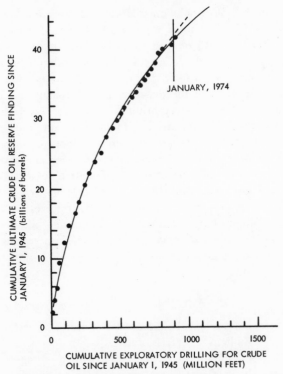

Figure 3-2. Relationship between cumulative oil finds and cumulative exploratory drilling.

where F_g = the cumulative discoveries of natural gas reserve findings in billions of standard cubic feet, and

X_g = the same basis of measurement as for crude oil.

The t-statistic for the estimated regression coefficient is again highly significant for Equation (3-6). Again, b_o was selected to minimize the indicated serial correlation.

Careful examination of the data displayed in Figure 3-2 shows a higher finding rate for 1962-1974 than for 1945-1974. One plausible explanation for this higher finding rate was the increasing economic incentive to explore for natural gas and crude oil. Another plausible explanation for this higher finding rate was improvements in exploration technology. We regard increasing incentives, rather than improving technologies, as the primary factor for higher finding rates.

Because of the higher finding rate for 1962-1974, Equation (3-5) was estimated for that period, too. The resulting estimate was:

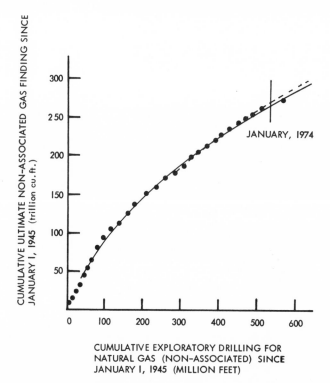

Figure 3-3. Relationship between cumulative gas finds and cumulative gas drilling.

$$(\log F_o - 5.561)^2 = -17.40 + \quad 6.3548 \log X_o \qquad (3\text{-}7)$$
$$(-12.28) \quad (29.64)$$
$$R^2 = 0.9865 \quad DW = 0.855$$

Equation (3-7) is shown as a dashed line in Figure 3-2.

To allow for the possibility of a higher gas finding rate for this period, as well as a higher oil finding rate, Equation (3-6) was also reestimated for natural gas for 1962-1974. The resulting estimate was:

$$(\log F_g - 7.522)^2 = -14.5383 + \quad 6.2596 \log X_g \qquad (3\text{-}8)$$
$$(-18.91) \quad (49.31)$$
$$R^2 = 0.9951 \quad DW = 1.446$$

Equation (3-8) is shown as a dashed line in Figure 3-3.

The finding rate for oil for 1945-1975 may be found by taking the first derivative of cumulative oil finds with respect to cumulative oil drilling in Equation (3-5). Similarly, the finding rate for gas in this 30-year period

Table 3-3. Regional Multiplying Factor for Crude Oil and Non-Associated Gas*

NPC Region	Crude Oil				Non-Associated Gas			
	Total† Reserve Found (10⁹ bbl)	Total Exploratory Drilling Footage (× 10⁶ ft)	Average Finding Rate (bbl/ft)	Regional Multiplying Factor	Total† Reserve Found (Tscf)	Total Exploratory Drilling Footage (× 10⁶ ft)	Average Finding Rate (Mcf/ft)	Regional Multiplying Factor
2	0.700	8.517	82.19	2.478	1.49	4.95	301.9	0.966
3	0.507	9.572	52.97	1.604	0.94	4.13	227.2	0.727
4	1.370	53.990	25.38	0.768	3.09	13.73	225.3	0.720
5	1.058	35.325	29.95	0.907	16.74	20.77	805.7	2.577
6	1.621	60.057	26.99	0.817	20.38	101.59	200.6	0.642
7	0.764	38.955	19.61	0.594	12.33	29.70	415.1	1.327
8, 9, 10	0.429	11.358	37.77	1.143	5.23	15.82	330.7	1.058
11	—	—	—	—	—	—	—	—
Coterminous U.S. (avg.)	7.005	212.94	33.03	—	61.89	197.28	312.7	—

* Data source: API (1975) and see footnote to Table 2-4.
† Ultimate Reserve Finding after applying Hubbert's Revision Factors.

Table 3-4. Initial Crude Oil and Non-Associated Gas Finding Rates by Regions per Foot of Exploratory Drilling

Region	Crude Oil (bbl/ft)		Non-Associated Gas (Mcf/ft)	
	U of Houston*	FEA†	U of Houston**	FEA‡
2	72.1	75.7	300	242
3	46.5	37.4	226	529
4	22.3	9.6	224	237
5	26.3	22.0	801	526
6	23.7	25.6	200	296
7	17.2	17.5	412	468
8, 9, 10	33.1	26.0	329	345
11	33.1	31.4	44	44

*Initial Finding Rate of 29 bbl/ft for U.S. multiplied by regional factors in Table 3.3.
†1976 FEA Oil Model; private communication, oil-in-place multiplied by primary recovery factor in Table 2.22.
**Initial Finding Rate of 311 bbl/ft for U.S. multiplied by regional factors in Table 3.3.
‡1976 FEA Gas Model; private communication, gas finding rate multiplied by TDRG (Table 2.7) to convert the finding rate from per foot of total drilling to per foot of exploratory drilling.

may be found by taking the first derivative of cumulative gas finds with respect to cumulative gas drilling in Equation (3-6). These two derivatives are respectively used to project low finding rates for oil and gas in Chapter 5.

High finding rates for oil and gas are projected for the analysis in Chapter 5 by taking the respective first derivative of cumulative finds with respect to cumulative drilling in Equations (3-7) and (3-8). The combination of the high and low finding rates found in this way is believed to bracket the likely range of finding rates for oil and gas in the remainder of this century.

Regional finding rates for crude oil and non-associated gas are found from the average U.S. finding rates by use of the regional multiplication factors given in Table 3-3. These regional factors were derived as the ratios of average regional finding rates and the average U.S. finding rates for 1966-1974. Table 3-4 shows the regional finding rates of our study (for the high case) are generally similar to the regional finding rates of FEA's *National Energy Outlook* (1976).

4

Normative Model for Exploratory Drilling

For specified economic conditions, the terminal finding rates for oil and gas production determine how much additional exploratory drilling will be required to reach the extensive margin of exploration for new oil and gas reserves. The drilling industry will respond to the economic demands of the oil and gas industries for exploratory drilling by maximizing the profits of supplying drilling services to fulfill the drilling requirements.

Profits to the drilling industry are measured in terms of the discounted stream of net revenues (or net present value). Drilling costs per foot are held constant at the 1974 level of average costs per foot drilled. An investment in drilling capacity is fully utilized throughout its service life of ten years, as assumed by FEA (1974, 1976). Accordingly, revenues from an investment in new drilling capacity are a constant percentage of investment. The time value of money stimulates the drilling industry to add drilling capacity whenever demand exists for additional capacity. However, as observed in the favorable expansion from 1946-1957, the drilling industry needs time to respond to increased demand for exploratory drilling services. A limitation on drilling capacity is imposed at two different levels in Chapter 5 to show the effects of this bottleneck in fulfilling exploratory drilling requirements of the oil and gas industry.

With the path of exploratory drilling services determined, the next task is to split this total drilling footage into exploratory drilling for gas and exploratory drilling for oil. Historical data show a high correlation between the ratio of exploratory drilling for oil relative to exploratory drilling for gas and the profitability of oil exploration relative to the profitability of gas exploration. Use of this correlation provides a systematic way to split total exploratory drilling into oil and gas drilling as the profitability of oil to gas exploration changes each year of the forecast period.

Next, the national split factor for exploratory drilling is adjusted, in accordance with historical data, to estimate the split factors for the major production regions. Also, historical patterns of regional drilling from 1966-1973 are used to allocate U.S. exploratory drilling footage to the major production regions. The regional allocations of drilling footage are then split into oil and gas exploratory drilling by use of the regional split factors. Regional allocations and split factors are explained in Section 4.4.

4.1. Normative Model for Exploratory Drilling Requirements

The drilling industry will use existing capacity to fulfill drilling requirements if total exploratory drilling requirements (TXDD) are less than the supply of exploratory drilling services (TXDF°) available as of January 1, 1974. However, if TXDD is greater than TXDF°, the drilling industry will invest in additional capacity to the extent needed to fulfill demand. New capacity added in year i (XDF(i)) is assumed to have a service life of y_d years, which starts in year i + 1. Full utilization is assumed of all new capacity throughout its service life.

The drilling industry can not expand immediately to fulfill an increase in demand for exploratory drilling. This limitation is specified here to have the following form in year i:

$$XDF(i) \leq \theta \cdot TXDF(i), \qquad (4\text{-}1)$$

where TXDF(i) is total exploratory drilling capacity existing in year i and θ is the upper bound for drilling capacity expansion.

TXDF(i) represents all undepreciated drilling capacity available to supply drilling services in year i. This useable drilling capacity is the sum of the undepreciated capacity existing January 1, 1974, plus the undepreciated capacity added after January 1, 1974:

$$TXDF(i) = TXDF° [1 - (i-1)/y_d] + \sum_{k=1}^{i-1} XDF(k), \qquad (4\text{-}2)$$

if $1 \leq i \leq y_d$, or

$$TXDF(i) = \sum_{k=i-y_d}^{i-1} XDF(k), \qquad \text{if } i > y_d,$$

where   i = 1 for 1974,   i = 2 for 1975, ...

New drilling capacity added in year i will require an investment of $\phi \cdot XDF(i)$ in the ith year, where ϕ is the per unit investment cost of drilling capacity. The initial cash outflow in year i after deducting the tax credit (t_c) per dollar invested is $(1 - t_c)\phi \cdot XDF(i)$. Investment in new capacity generates a gross revenue stream of $\zeta \cdot XDF(i)$ per year from year $i + 1$ through $y_d + i$, where ζ is the revenue per unit of capacity. Letting E represent the fraction of the gross revenue needed to cover operating costs, the net revenue before income tax is $(1 - E)\,\zeta \cdot XDF(i)$. Depreciation in each year i of the service life is $\phi \cdot XDF(i)/y_d$. An investment in new drilling capacity in year i gives the following net income (after corporate income taxes) per unit of drilling capacity:

$$NR(k) = \zeta(1\text{-}E) - t\,[\zeta - \zeta E - \phi/y_d], \qquad (4\text{-}3)$$
$$k = i + 1, \ldots, i + y_d,$$

where t is the corporate income tax rate.

The net present value, $CV(i)$, per unit of new drilling capacity in year i is obtained by discounting the net cash flow after taxes back to the present:

$$CV(i) = -\frac{(1 - t_c)\,\phi}{(1 + r)^{\,i - 0.5}} + \sum_{k = i + 1}^{i + y_d} \frac{NR(k)}{(1 + r)^{\,k - 0.5}} \qquad (4\text{-}4)$$

Investment in new exploratory drilling capacity is continued to the level where services of exploratory drilling equipment are just adequate to fulfill total exploratory drilling requirements TXDD.

$$\sum_{i = 1}^{T_d} TXDF(i) = TXDD, \qquad (4\text{-}5)$$

where $T_d - 1$ is the last year for investment,

Mathematically, the profit-maximizing model for the drilling industry may be stated as follows:

$$\text{Maximize } Z = \sum_{i = 1}^{T_d} CV(i) \cdot XDF(i), \qquad (4\text{-}6)$$

with respect to XDF subject to Equations (4-1), (4-2), and (4-5).

4.2.   Values of the Parameters for Drilling Model

The annual revenue stream for the initial investment as of January 1, 1974, was calculated in the following way. In 1974, the average drilling rig with a capability of drilling a 7,000-ft well cost around $1 million (Surratt, 1975). This typical rig drills on the average 90,000 ft/yr (Baker, 1976). Drilling costs in 1974 were $28.90/ft. Drilling contractors received 36.1% of the drilling costs paid (Independent Petroleum Association of America, 1976). This fee gave an annual gross revenue per rig of $940,000. Drilling cost outlays paid by the contractor are assumed to be 75% of the gross revenues ($E = .75$), leaving 25% of gross revenues to cover initial investment costs.

Assumed values for the tax credit, corporate tax rate, and the discount rate were 7%, 50%, and 10%, respectively. Initial drilling capacity in 1974 was 47.8×10^6 ft of actual exploratory drilling footage.

Given a set of values for the economic parameters, the model may be used to estimate total exploratory drilling requirements. Estimates of exploratory drilling requirements are provided in Chapter 5 for different specifications of the economic parameters, tax provisions, finding rate projections, and drilling capacity availabilities.

4.3.   Split of Total Exploratory Drilling into Oil and Gas Exploration

Historically, the percentage of total exploratory drilling footage classified as successful oil wells has trended downward from a high of around 80% in the early 1950s to a low of nearly 40% in the early 1970s. This downward trend in the split of total exploratory drilling into oil rather than gas wells was found to be highly correlated with the increased profitability of exploratory drilling for gas relative to oil.

In our study, the profitability of oil relative to gas exploration was correlated with the successful exploratory drilling footage for oil relative to gas for 1965-1975 as a means of splitting the total demand requirements for exploratory drilling into that for oil and for gas. This profitability index was calculated using the model described in Chapter 2 except depreciation allowances and production expenses were ignored to reflect the fact that the natural gas industry was operating at a level below the profit-maximizing rate of production (depletion rate); see Appendix II for exact mathematical procedures and data used to estimate the split factors for the nation.

Figure 4-1 shows historical split factors plotted against the lagged relative profitability index for 1948-1975. Clearly, 1948-1964 data are different from 1965-1975 data. Figure 4-1 shows that for the same RPI more gas well exploration occurred recently than previously. This structural change coin-

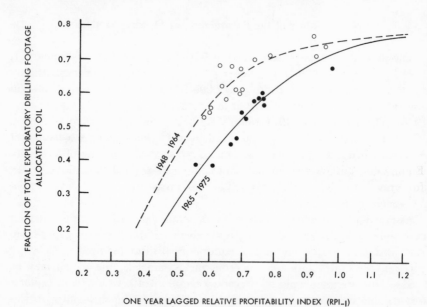

ONE YEAR LAGGED RELATIVE PROFITABILITY INDEX (RPI₋ₗ)

Figure 4-1. Fraction of total exploratory drilling footage (split factor) allocated to oil exploration—low long-term finding rates.

cides with a rapid market expansion of natural gas use in the mid-1960s. The following regression equation was fitted to the data:

$$\log (1/S - a_0) = a_1 + a_2 \log RPI_{-1}, \qquad (4\text{-}7)$$

where S is the split factor for oil and RPI_{-1} means one period of lagged RPI.

For 1948-1964 data and the low finding rates for gas and oil, the results were:

$$\log (1/S - 1.26) = -2.930 - \quad 4.330 \log RPI_{-1} \qquad (4\text{-}8)$$
$$(-11.344) \quad (-6.384)$$
$$R^2 = 0.7261 \quad DW = 1.21$$

where t-values are in parentheses.

For 1965-1975 data and the low finding rate for gas and oil, the results were:

$$\log (1/S - 1.20) = -1.712 - \quad 3.797 \log RPI_{-1} \qquad (4\text{-}9)$$
$$(-10.625) \quad (-8.921)$$
$$R^2 = 0.8871 \quad DW = 2.30$$

For 1965-1975 data and an assumed high finding rate for oil (Equation (3-7)) and for gas (Equation (3-8)), a new split factor equation results:

$$S = -0.3334 + 0.9747\,RPI_{-1} \qquad (4\text{-}10)$$
$$(-2.788) \qquad (7.130)$$
$$R^2 = 0.833 \qquad DW = 1.62$$

Figure 4-2 shows historical split factors for 1965-1975 when high finding Equations (3-7) and (3-8) were used to estimate long-term finding rates for oil and gas.

Significant differences clearly exist between Equations (4-8) and (4-9). Equation (4-9) is used to forecast the split of total exploratory drilling footage into oil and gas footage in Chapter 5 for the low finding rate case; and Equation (4-10) is used to forecast this split for the high finding rate case.

Historically, the maximum split factor for oil was 0.775 (observed in 1951), and the minimum split factor for oil was 0.384 (observed in 1973). The minimum split factor for oil in the future was assumed to be 0.20. This assumption reflects the fact that some oil will be found in the search for gas, even if the profitability of gas is high relative to oil. A maximum split factor for oil of 0.83 is implicit in Equation (4-9), and a maximum split factor for oil of 0.8 is assumed for Equation (4-10).

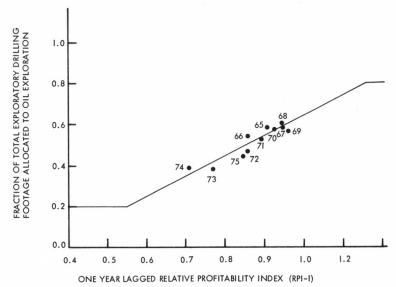

Figure 4-2. Fraction of total exploratory drilling footage (split factor) allocated to oil exploration—high long-term finding rates.

Table 4-1. Historical Allocation Pattern of Exploratory Drilling Footage to Different Regions of Lower 48 States*

| Year | \multicolumn{8}{c}{Region} | | | | | | | |
	2	3	4	5	6	7	8, 9, 10	11
1966	0.0360	0.0226	0.1066	0.1531	0.4293	0.1763	0.0748	0.0013
1967	0.0427	0.0242	0.1203	0.1431	0.4268	0.1763	0.0654	0.0012
1968	0.0392	0.0186	0.1834	0.1218	0.3999	0.1730	0.0632	0.0009
1969	0.0298	0.0357	0.2080	0.1274	0.3825	0.1667	0.0491	0.0009
1970	0.0339	0.0370	0.2111	0.1255	0.3661	0.1708	0.0536	0.0019
1971	0.0294	0.0565	0.1750	0.1245	0.3801	0.1705	0.619	0.0022
1972	0.0250	0.0496	0.1733	0.1263	0.3737	0.1641	0.0608	0.0273
1973	0.0310	0.0359	0.1529	0.1511	0.3943	0.1957	0.0734	0.0057
1974	0.0280	0.0289	0.1505	0.1548	0.3875	0.1526	0.0137	0.0049
Values used in model	0.0328	0.0343	0.1646	0.1364	0.3934	0.1673	0.0662	0.0050

*Data source: See footnote to Table 2-4.

Table 4-2. Normalized Fraction of Exploratory Drilling Footage Allocated to Oil Exploration (Split Factor) by Regions*

| Year | \multicolumn{8}{c}{Region} | | | | | | | | U.S. Avg. |
	2	3	4	5	6	7	8, 9, 10	11	
1966	1.0360	1.4063	1.6167	1.3827	0.7843	0.8079	1.0244	—	0.5177†
1967	0.9693	1.2429	1.4791	1.1926	0.7527	1.0680	0.9916	—	0.5981
1968	1.0215	1.1597	1.4136	1.1912	0.7866	1.0949	0.7123	—	0.6239
1969	1.2917	1.2619	1.5277	1.2986	0.6221	1.1742	0.6203	—	0.5704
1970	1.2923	1.3335	1.4641	1.2280	0.7871	1.0010	0.4877	—	0.5829
1971	1.3868	1.1675	1.2539	1.2835	0.6450	1.2114	0.9840	—	0.5479
1972	1.2815	1.6771	1.5529	1.1577	0.5501	1.0751	0.8351	—	0.4757
1973	1.2769	1.5293	1.7646	1.0228	0.7360	1.2969	0.8261	—	0.3849
1974	1.6331	1.3371	1.7260	1.1094	0.6840	1.3264	0.8033	—	0.3890
Values used in model	1.2466	1.3461	1.5332	1.2074	0.7053	1.1173	0.8094	1.6000**	—

*Data source: See footnote to Table 2-4.
†The last column shows the fraction of total exploratory drilling footage in the lower 48 states that is allocated to oil exploration. Other columns show the regional split factor divided by the U.S. split factor in the last column.
**Value arbitrarily assigned.

4.4. Regional Exploratory Drilling

The percentages of the total exploratory drilling in the nation done in each major production region from 1966-1974 are summarized in Table 4-1. These percentages appear to be relatively constant throughout this period; accordingly, the average percentage for this period was used to allocate U.S. total exploratory drilling footage to the regions.

Similarly, the normalized regional split factors for oil and gas in Table 4-2 are relatively constant for 1966-1974. Regional averages for this period (γ_j) were also used to calculate regional split factors (S_j) from national split factors:

$$S_j = \gamma_j \cdot S \qquad (4\text{-}11)$$

Regional split factors were restricted between 0.05 and 0.95. Future econometric analysis might well be directed to explaining the regional split factors.

5

Model Results for Crude Oil and Natural Gas Production from New Reserves in the Lower 48 States

This chapter shows how different prices, tax provisions, finding rate projections, and drilling capacity limitations will affect terminal finding rates, ultimate economic reserves, depletion rates, production paths, and supply functions for crude oil and natural gas production from new reserves in the lower 48 states. The following price relationships, tax provisions, finding rates, and drilling capacity limitations are considered in the analysis.

Price Relationships

1. A fixed price ratio of 1:10 for the price of natural gas ($/Mcf) relative to the price of crude oil ($/bbl);
2. A fixed price ratio of 1:6 for the price of natural gas ($/Mcf) relative to the price of crude oil ($/bbl).

Tax Provisions

1. No depletion allowance and current deduction of intangible and dry-hole drilling costs;
2. No depletion allowance and amortization of intangible and dry-hole drilling costs;
3. A 22% depletion allowance and current deduction of intangible and dry-hole drilling costs.

Finding Rate Projections

1. A high finding rate projection representing the rate of change of cumulative finds vs. cumulative exploratory drilling in the lower 48 states from 1962-1974;
2. A low finding rate projection representing the rate of change of cumulative finds vs. cumulative exploratory drilling in the lower 48 states from 1945-1974.

Limitations on Drilling Capacity Expansion

1. Drilling capacity can not expand faster than 14% per year;
2. Drilling capacity can not expand faster than 25% per year.

In all evaluations, the natural gas liquids price is 69.7% of the crude oil price. All prices and costs are expressed in 1974 dollars to remove the influence of inflation. A uniform discount rate of 10% is assumed for the nation and all regions of the nation.

The combination of price relationships, tax provisions, finding rates, and capacity limitations analyzed was:

	Cases Studied					
	I	II	III	IV	V	VI
Price Relationships	1	1	1	1	2	1
Tax Provisions	1	1	3	2	1	1
Finding Rate	1	2	1	2	1	1
Drilling Capacity	1	1	1	1	1	2

Case I was formulated as the base case to reflect expected price relationships, current tax provisions, and recent finding rate trends. Deductions for intangible and dry-hole drilling costs are still allowed; however, depletion allowances for oil and gas producers were generally discontinued in 1975. The projection basis for the high finding rate gives a January 1, 1974, estimate of 29 barrels of crude oil per foot of exploratory drilling. This 1974 estimate corresponds well with Hubbert's 1972 estimate of 30 barrels per foot drilled, as reported recently in the *Oil and Gas Journal* (Oct. 11, 1976). Also, this high projection basis gives a January 1, 1974, finding rate estimate for non-associated natural gas of 314 Mcf per foot of exploratory drilling.

A uniform discount rate for the nation and all regions of the nation is in accordance with Hausman's review (1975) of the Project Independence Study (FEA, 1974). The 10% discount rate assumes high prime interest rates will generally prevail in the rest of this century.

A 14% limitation on drilling capacity expansion was assumed in the base case. This 14% upper bound reflects the average annual rate of capacity expansion in the favorable period of high incentives in the 1950s.

The low finding rate basis in Case II gives less optimistic forecasts of oil supplies than the high finding rate basis in Case I. This low finding rate basis, which reflects the 30-year historical trend from 1945-1974, gives a January 1, 1974, estimate of 22 barrels of crude oil per foot of exploratory drilling. Also, this low finding rate projection basis gives a January 1, 1974, finding rate estimate for natural gas (non-associated) of 298 Mcf per foot of exploratory drilling.

The tax provisions of Case III show the supply consequences of reinstituting the 22% depletion allowance and continuing intangible and dry-hole drilling cost deductions as current expenses. Case I compared with Case III shows the exploration, development, and production consequences of recent policy decisions to discontinue the depletion allowance.

Case IV was specified to show how policy action to amortize intangible and dry-hole drilling costs will generally contract exploratory drilling, reserve development, and petroleum production from the low levels of Case II.

Cases I, II, III, and IV are given primary emphasis in the analysis of this chapter. Case V was formulated to show the production and supply consequences of policy actions to price natural gas at the Btu equivalent of crude oil, as suggested by Hausman (1975). Case VI shows the supply effects of fewer drilling capacity bottlenecks than assumed in Case I.

The results of the evaluations are organized to show (1) how different tax provisions and finding rate projections will affect the extensive margin of exploration and the intensive margin of development and (2) how these tax provisions and finding rate projections will affect the estimates of economically recoverable reserves. Comparisons are made between the reserve estimates of our study and those of the U.S. Geological Survey (USGS), the National Petroleum Council, and the Mobil Oil Corporation (Miller et al., 1975).

With industry maximizing profits at the extensive margin of exploration and the intensive margin of development, the next task is to show the production path and supply function consequences of the different policy, technical, and economic considerations in Cases I-VI. For 1974-2002, production paths for crude oil and natural gas are projected to show how production from new reserves will be affected over time by different pricing, taxing, and finding rate considerations. Supply functions are estimated for 1985 and 1995 to show how the quantities supplied of crude oil and natural gas from new reserves are affected by crude oil and natural gas prices in each of these years. Estimates are also made to show how shifts in the supply curves are affected by different tax policies and finding rate projections.

5.1. Diminishing Marginal Returns, Terminal Finding Rates, and Economic Additions to Reserves

With cumulative increases in the exploratory footage drilled for crude oil, the finding rate projection of Case I in Figure 5-1 decreases rapidly from 29 barrels of oil per foot drilled at 866.4 million feet of exploratory drilling to 11.7 barrels of oil per foot drilled at 5,000 million feet of

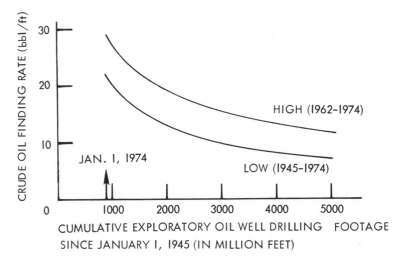

Figure 5-1. *Crude oil finding rates vs. cumulative oil exploratory drilling footage.*

exploratory drilling. This striking illustration of diminishing marginal returns in oil exploration is further demonstrated for the finding rate projection of Case II, where the finding rate decreases from 22 barrels of crude oil per foot drilled at 866.4 million feet of exploratory drilling to seven barrels of oil per foot drilled at 5,000 million feet of exploratory drilling.

In Case I, a crude oil price of $7/bbl is needed in the model to achieve a terminal finding rate of 29 barrels per foot of exploratory drilling; and a crude oil price of $14/bbl is needed to achieve a terminal finding rate of 14.3 barrels per foot of exploratory drilling; see Figure 5-2.

At each expected crude oil price, the terminal finding rate represents the extensive margin of exploration where the marginal value of the production from the newly found reserves just equals the marginal costs of exploratory drilling, development, and production.

Summing the area under the high finding rate curve in Figure 5-1 from the estimated finding rate of 29 barrels per foot of exploratory drilling (January 1, 1974) to a terminal finding rate of 14.3 barrels per foot of exploratory drilling gives 51 billion barrels of economically recoverable additions to crude oil reserves in the lower 48 states. This level of reserves is slightly less than the mean estimate of reserve additions made by the USGS in 1975; see Figure 5-3. If the USGS probability distribution of finding rates is superimposed at the estimate in Case I for $14/bbl, the range of reserve additions found in this study is shifted downward by 4 billion barrels from the range of reserve estimates found by the USGS.

The results of our study further show how different tax provisions and pricing policies affect the terminal finding rates; see Figure 5-2. For each crude oil price, the 22% depletion allowance in Case III allows the extensive margin of exploration to be pushed further in attaining a lower terminal finding rate than the zero depletion allowance in Case I. Similarly, for each crude oil price, current deductions of intangible and dry-hole drilling costs in Case II permit a lower terminal finding rate than the amortized deductions of intangible and dry-hole drilling costs in Case IV.

Alternatively, attainment of a desired level of oil exploration marked by a terminal finding rate requires a higher oil price with a zero depletion allowance (Case I) than with a 22% depletion allowance (Case III). Still higher oil prices must be paid to attain the same desired level of oil exploration and terminal finding rate with amortization of all drilling costs (Case IV) than with current deductions of intangible and dry-hole drilling costs (Case II).

Also, the results of our study show how different tax provisions, pricing policies, and finding rate projections affect the estimates of additions to crude oil reserves; see Figure 5-3. The favorable tax provisions and high finding rate projection basis of Case III give the largest estimates of reserve

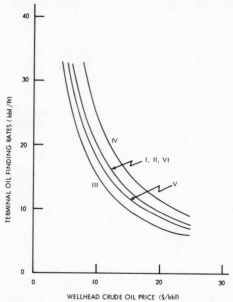

Figure 5-2. Terminal finding rates for crude oil.

additions, while the unfavorable tax provisions and low finding rate projection basis of Case IV give the smallest estimates of reserve additions for every crude oil price considered.

With crude oil prices ranging from $10 to $14/bbl, the range of reserve addition estimates in our study varies from a low of virtually zero to a high of around 80 billion barrels for the different scenarios. This range of estimates encompasses Mobil's 1974 estimate (15 billion barrels), the 1975 range of USGS estimates (40.2 to 75.2 billion barrels), and the NPC's 1973 estimate (45 billion barrels) (Miller et al., 1975). However, none of our reserve estimates at prices of crude oil less than $20/bbl is even close to Commoner's estimates (325 billion barrels) (Commoner, 1976).

Two important points are clearly evident from the crude oil reserve estimates made in our study. First, estimates of reserve additions for crude oil will be greatly affected by the taxing and pricing policies allowed by government decision-makers. Second, as long maintained by Hubbert, diminishing finding rates are a technical fact of life with increased exploratory drilling for crude oil in the lower 48 states.

Another point of interest is the price elasticity for additions to crude oil reserves in Epple's study and in our study. Case III is comparable in terms of tax policies to the period studied by Epple. Epple's estimate gives a price elasticity of 2.9 for 1947-1968 if trend considerations are ignored; our results show a price elasticity of 2.0 for $11/bbl in Case III. This price elasticity decreases gradually as the crude oil price increases. Epple's higher price elasticity may have resulted from the lower price imbedded in the historical data.

Basically, the same procedure used for crude oil was utilized for natural gas (non-associated) to project finding rates and to estimate terminal finding rates and economic additions to natural gas reserves. The high and low finding rate projections used are shown in Figure 5-4 for a range of cumulative footage of exploratory drilling. Again, the inescapable principle of diminishing returns is clearly evident with the finding rate falling in both cases from around 300 Mcf per foot of exploratory drilling at 550 million feet of cumulative exploratory drilling to nearly 100 Mcf per foot of exploratory drilling at 4,500 million feet of cumulative exploratory drilling.

The wellhead prices of natural gas needed to achieve a given terminal finding rate are given in Figure 5-5 for all six cases studied. Our estimates show a natural gas price of $.70/Mcf is required in Case I to push the extensive margin to a terminal finding rate of 314 Mcf per foot of exploratory drilling (the finding rate at the beginning of 1974). Also, our estimates show a natural gas price of $1.45/Mcf is needed in Case I to achieve a terminal finding rate of 150 Mcf per foot of exploratory drilling.

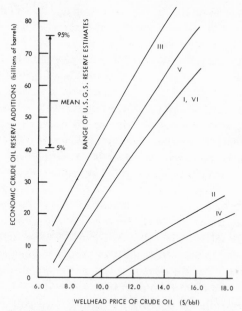

Figure 5-3. Economic crude oil reserve additions for lower 48 states.

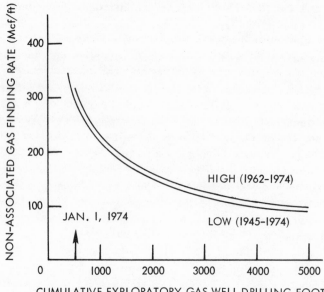

CUMULATIVE EXPLORATORY GAS WELL DRILLING FOOTAGE

SINCE JANUARY 1, 1945 (IN MILLION FEET)

Figure 5-4. Non-associated gas finding rates vs. cumulative gas exploratory drilling footage.

Summation of the area under the high finding rate curve in Figure 5-5 from 314 to 150 Mcf per foot of exploratory drilling gives a reserve estimate of 345 billion cubic feet of natural gas. In Figure 5-6, our reserve addition estimate for natural gas at $1.45/Mcf in Case I is slightly above the mean estimate made by the USGS. Again, superimposing USGS's probability distribution of reserve additions at our estimate gives a range of reserve additions in Case I ($1.45/Mcf natural gas) similar to the range of estimates reported by the USGS (Miller et al., 1975).

Our results further show how different tax provisions, pricing policies, and economic conditions affect the estimates of natural gas prices required to achieve different terminal finding rates. The terminal finding rate, as for crude oil, determines the estimate of additions to natural gas reserves. Again, greatly different estimates of reserve additions are found for variations in the assumed tax, price, technical, and economic conditions. For each price studied from $.80 to $2/Mcf, the largest estimate of reserve additions was found in Case III; the smallest estimate of reserve additions was found in Case IV. Estimates of reserve additions ranged from near zero in Case IV at a natural gas price of $.80/Mcf to around 750 trillion cubic feet in Case III at a natural gas price of $2/Mcf. This range of reserve additions for natural gas encompasses the 1975 range of USGS estimates (261 to 406 trillion cubic feet), the 1972 estimate (600 trillion cubic feet), and the 1974 Mobil estimate (60 trillion cubic feet); see Miller et al., (1975) and NPC (1972).

Our estimates of additions to reserves for gas are more optimistic than USGS estimates of additions to reserves for gas. The USGS evidently assumed a low price for gas relative to oil. As for crude oil, Epple's estimated price elasticity (2.9) for additions to natural gas reserves (non-associated) is higher than our estimated price elasticity (1.6) for additions to natural gas reserves (non-associated) in Case III at a gas price of $1.40/Mcf.

As shown for crude oil, the estimates of reserve additions for natural gas are affected greatly by government tax policy, natural gas prices, and economic conditions. These factors have much greater effects on reserve additions than the estimated statistical error in the finding rate reported by the USGS (Miller et al., 1975).

5.2.   Path of Exploratory Drilling

Figure 5-7 shows two paths of exploratory drilling for two different price combinations ($8/bbl and $0.80/Mcf, $14/bbl and $1.40/Mcf) in Case I. For the $14/bbl and $1.40/Mcf price combination, total exploratory drilling requirements for both crude oil and natural gas are estimated at $5,086 \times 10^6$ ft. This estimate of requirements uses (1) Figures 5-2 and 5-5 to obtain the terminal finding rates for oil and gas at the specified prices, and (2) Figures 5-1 and 5-4 to give the cumulative exploratory drilling footages for oil and gas required to reach these terminal finding rates. In 1974, total exploratory drilling footage was 47.8×10^6 to correspond to the initial projection point of our study. The models show exploratory drilling footage will increase at the compound rate (corresponding to the upper bound) of 14% per year until 1988. Exploratory drilling footage increases at a lesser rate in 1989; after 1989, investment in additional exploratory drilling capacity ceases. This stock of capacity is adequate to drill out the remaining drilling requirements at the extensive margin of exploration. All the drilling capacity is fully depreciated out in 1999 when the extensive margin is attained.

For the $8/bbl and $.80/Mcf price combination, total exploratory drilling requirements are estimated at 560×10^6 ft. The drilling industry expanded

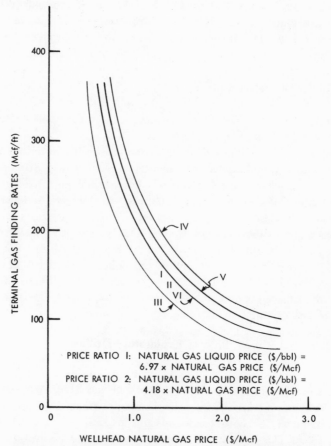

Fig. 5-5. Terminal finding rates for non-associated gas.

in this case at the compound rate of 14% per year until 1976. Remaining drilling prospects are drilled out with use of this capacity. The extensive margin of exploration is reached in 1986.

Figure 5-7 illustrates the critical importance of the price assumptions in forecasting exploratory drilling. The FEA's imposed drilling path in its 1974 study for the Business-As-Usual case is given for comparison purposes; it implies a 6.3% rate of annual growth in exploratory drilling footage. Actual data points are provided for 1975 and 1976. Clearly, the drilling path is extremely sensitive to the price assumptions made.

5.3. Annual Depletion Rates and National Split Factors

The maximum value for the annual depletion rate represents the intensive margin of development, where the marginal returns from accelerating

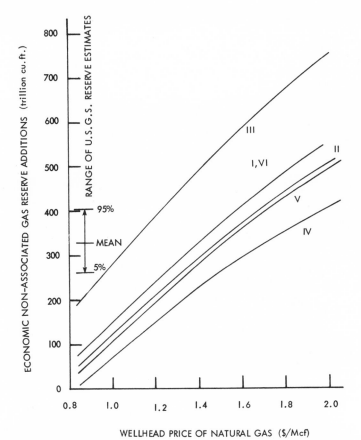

WELLHEAD PRICE OF NATURAL GAS ($/Mcf)

Fig. 5-6. Economic non-associated gas reserve additions for lower 48 states.

production equals the marginal investment costs of developing the production. For a crude oil price of $12/bbl, Figure 5-8 shows how the net present value (NPV) per foot of exploratory drilling first increases and then decreases for Cases I, II, III, and IV as the annual rate of depletion is parametrically increased in the model. The annual depletion rate maximizing the NPV for the high finding rate projection basis is 6.4% in Case I (zero depletion allowance and high finding rate projection). Visualizing reinstitution of the 22% depletion allowance for tax purposes resulted in a higher optional depletion rate of 7.3% in Case III. In contrast, assuming a lower finding rate projection basis and a zero depletion allowance in the second case decreased the profit-maximizing depletion rate from 6.4% in Case I to 5.3% in Case II. Amortization of intangible and dry-hole drilling

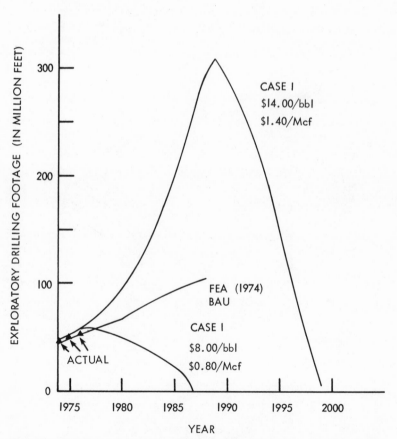

Fig. 5-7. Exploratory drilling footage projections in the lower 48 states.

costs, rather than current deductions of these costs, further reduces the maximum profitable rate of depletion from 5.3% in Case II to 4.9% in Case IV. As expected, depletion allowances and current deductions of dry-hole and intangible drilling costs accelerate the profit-maximizing rates of depleting a given crude oil reserve.

Annual depletion rates maximizing the NPV per foot of exploratory drilling for natural gas (non-associated) were also computed parametrically for a natural gas price of $1.20/Mcf; see Figure 5-9. Slightly higher profit-maximizing rates of annual depletion were found in every respective case for natural gas than for crude oil.

The depletion curves in Figure 5-8 relate directly to the theoretical formulation in Chapter 1. With a given case, the values of the parametric constants are fixed. The model estimates the functions $X = l(\alpha)$ and $d = m(\alpha)$, which are derived from the optimality conditions in Equation (1-8). Each curve in Figure 5-8 illustrates how NPV decreases from the optimum as non-optimal values of d are selected for $X = 866.4 \times 10^6$ ft. Similar illustrations could be developed for other values of X.

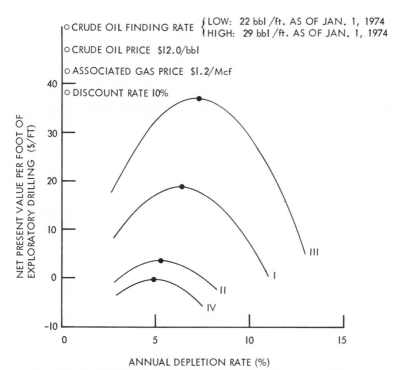

Figure 5-8. Profit maximizing depletion rates for crude oil development.

As indicated in Section 4.3, the national split of exploratory drilling into drilling for oil and drilling for gas is adjusted internally in the model as changes in the finding rates for oil and gas affect the profitability of oil relative to gas exploration. For a crude price of $14/bbl, Figure 5-10 shows how the national split factor in Case I continually increases the fraction of total exploratory drilling allocated to crude oil production from 1975-1997. Initially, only 27.5% of total exploratory drilling is allocated by the model to crude oil exploration, because the price of natural gas relative to crude oil is favorable in comparison to historical price relationships. However, relatively large allocations of exploratory drilling to gas rather than oil cause the natural gas finding rate to decline faster than the crude oil finding rate, which increases the profitability of oil exploration relative to gas exploration. The allocation of exploratory drilling to crude oil reaches a maximum of slightly above 40% in 1997. Similar adjustments in the national split factor are made in every case for different gas and oil prices.

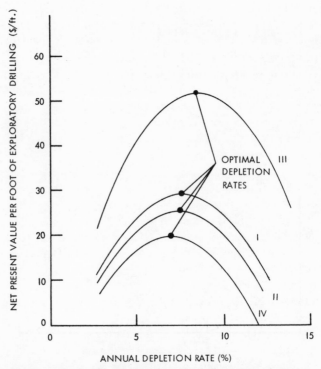

Figure 5-9. Profit maximizing depletion rates for non-associated gas development.

5.4.   Production Paths for Crude Oil and Natural Gas from New Reserves in the Lower 48 States

Figure 5-11 shows the production paths for Case I, where the crude oil price is $14/bb! and the natural gas price is $1.40/Mcf, versus Case V, where the crude oil price is $12/bbl and the natural gas price is $2/Mcf.

Crude oil production is greater in Case I than in Case V in every year for the rest of this century. Production increases at an increasing rate from the present to the mid-1980s because exploratory drilling footage increases; thereafter, production increases at a decreasing rate because exploratory drilling footage declines as illustrated in Figure 5-7. In Case V, production increases to 1.34 billion barrels in 2002; in Case I, production increases to 1.46 billion barrels in 2002.

Figure 5-12 shows how the projected production paths for crude oil, where the crude oil price is $14/bbl and the natural gas price is $1.40/Mcf in all cases, are affected by different depletion allowances, finding rate projections, and drilling cost deductions. Removal of the depletion allowance, as generally legislated in 1975, has a relatively small depressing effect on production for the high finding rate projection of Case I in the next 10 years; however, the effect of removing the depletion allowance becomes increasingly pronounced in the last 15 years of the twentieth century as the lower terminal finding rate allowed by the depletion allowance becomes increasingly important. Reinstitution of the depletion allowance would give, according to the model, around one billion barrels more oil from new reserves in the final year of production (2002) than continuation of the effective zero depletion allowance, as presently legislated.

Rapidly growing scarcities of oil supplies from new domestic onshore reserves will be facing the nation in the 1980s if the low finding rate projection of Case II materializes rather than the high finding rate projection of Case I. In Case II, production from new reserves begins increasing at a diminishing rate in the early 1980s and peaks at a relatively low level of 0.569 billion barrels in 2002. This peak level of production is around 891 million barrels per year below the 2002 level of production at the higher projected finding rate in Case I. Clearly, the nation needs to undertake an immediate in-depth, comprehensive effort to improve statistical estimates of the likely finding rate for a given set of economic conditions and policy considerations.

Discontinuation of deductions for intangible and dry-hole drilling costs as current expenses will further decrease production from new reserves in the lower 48 states. Around 264 million barrels less crude oil are produced per year at the turn of the century in Case IV than in Case II.

Similar production path relationships are shown in Figures 5-13 and 5-14 for non-associated natural gas production from new reserves in the lower 48 states. According to the model, the higher natural gas price and the lower crude oil price in Case V ($12/bbl and $2/Mcf) than in Case I ($14/bbl and $1.40/Mcf) stimulates increasingly greater production of natural gas in the next 20 years; see Figure 5-13. Production of non-associated natural gas from newly found reserves peaks at 18.4 trillion cubic feet in 1995 at a high of $2/Mcf in Case V. This peak level of production is 4.5 trillion cubic feet greater than the peak level of production (13.9 trillion cubic feet) found in Case I in 1993 at the lower $1.40/Mcf.

As found for crude oil production from new reserves, non-associated natural gas production from newly found reserves in the lower 48 states is significantly affected by the tax policies and finding rate projections assumed; see Figure 5-14. Differences in the production paths are the most pronounced in the declining phases of production in the last part

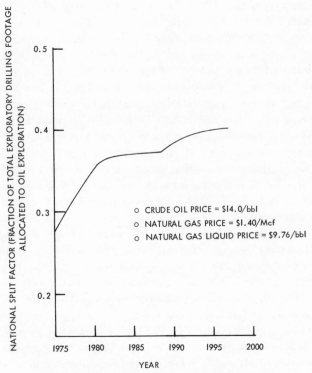

Figure 5-10. National split factor for Case I.

of this century and the beginning of the next century. An additional 6 trillion cubic feet of natural gas is produced in the peak year of Case III (1998) than in the peak year of Case I (1993). This 6 trillion cubic feet spread continues for the declining periods of production illustrated, when an effective transition to alternative energy resources must be underway.

Figure 5-15 shows how fewer bottlenecks in the supplying of drilling capacity to the petroleum industry will accelerate the production of natural gas between now and the early 1990s. Drilling capacity is allowed to expand at a maximum rate of 25% in Case VI and 14% in Case I. Production in Case VI reaches a peak of 16 trillion cubic feet in 1989 and falls rapidly thereafter. This peak level of production in Case VI is 4.1 trillion cubic feet greater than the production level in Case I. Production in Case I, which reaches the falling production level of Case VI in 1993, peaks at 14 trillion cubic feet in 1994.

5.5. Supply Functions for Crude Oil and Natural Gas from New Reserves in the Lower 48 States

The supply function for crude oil gives the quantity of crude oil produced as a function of the crude oil price, where the natural gas price and the prices of all other products are held constant; this is the economic supply of crude oil. Similarly, the supply function for natural gas (non-associated) gives the quantity of natural gas produced as a function of the natural gas price, where the crude oil price and the prices of all other products are held constant; this is the economic supply of natural gas.

Economic supplies of crude oil and natural gas from new reserves are estimated for the lower 48 states in 1985 and 1995. Initially, Case I conditions are assumed for tax provisions, finding rate projections, and drilling capacity limitations. The natural gas price is held constant at $1.40/Mcf in estimating the supply curves for crude oil; the crude oil price is held constant at $14/bbl in estimating the supply curves for natural gas. Comparisons are made between the estimates for 1985 of our study and the estimates for 1985 of FEA's two studies (1974, 1976). Finally, the shift effects on the economic supplies of crude oil and natural gas at different tax provisions and finding rate projections, as specified in Cases I, II, III, and IV, are estimated for 1985 and 1995.

With the natural gas price fixed at $1.40/Mcf and with Case I conditions otherwise, the economic supply curves for crude oil in the lower 48 states are shown in Figure 5-16 for 1985 and 1995. In 1985, the supply curve shows 0.143 billion barrels of crude oil will be produced from new reserves at $8/bbl; 0.425 billion barrels of crude oil will be produced

(text continued on page 65)

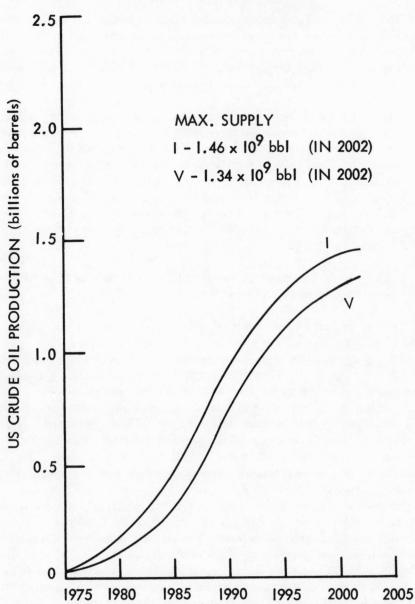

Figure 5-11. *Production paths for crude oil from new reserves in the lower 48 states for Case I vs. Case V.*

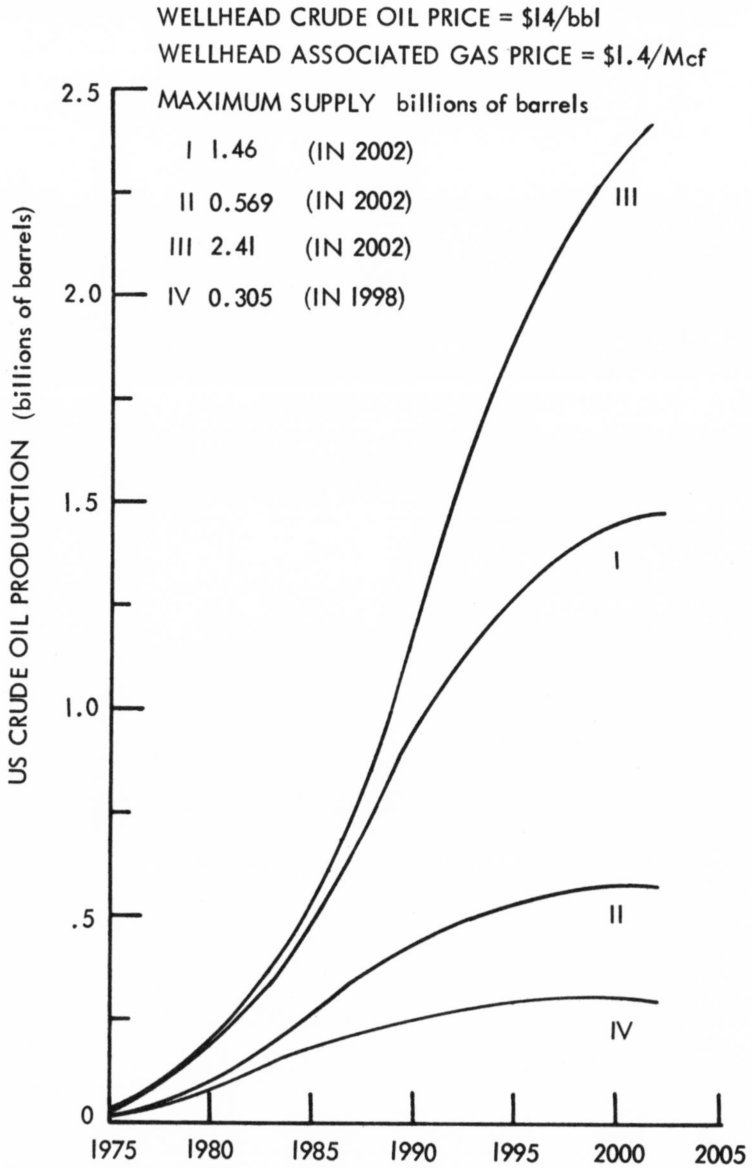

Figure 5-12. *Production paths for crude oil from new reserves in the lower 48 states for Cases I, II, III, and IV.*

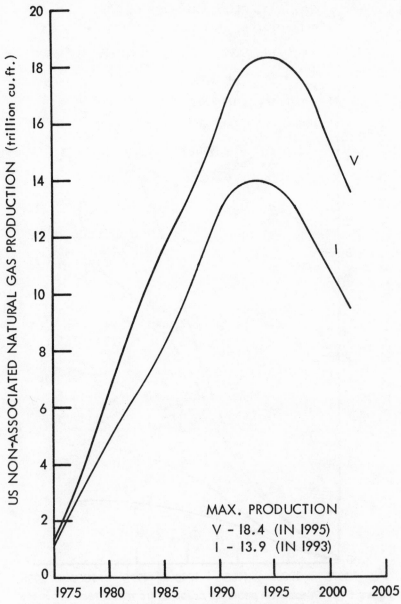

Figure 5-13. Non-associated natural gas production paths from new reserves in the lower 48 states for Cases I and V.

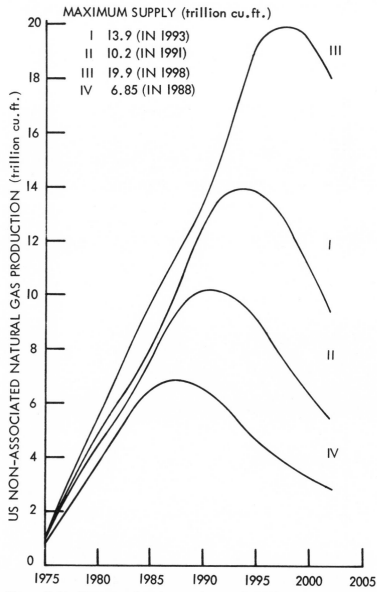

MAXIMUM SUPPLY (trillion cu.ft.)

I   13.9 (IN 1993)
II   10.2 (IN 1991)
III 19.9 (IN 1998)
IV   6.85 (IN 1988)

Figure 5-14. Non-associated natural gas production paths from new reserves in the lower 48 states for Cases I, II, III, and IV.

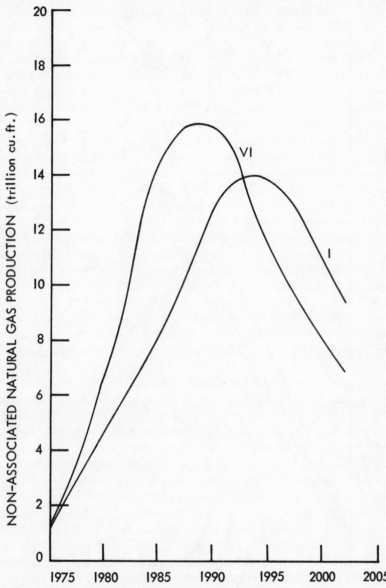

Figure 5-15. Non-associated natural gas production paths from new reserves in the lower 48 states for Cases I and VI.

at $13/bbl; and 0.631 billion barrels of crude oil will be produced at $18/bbl. Incrementally, the first $5 increase (from $8 to $13/bbl) gives 0.282 billion barrels of additional crude oil; the second $5 increase (from $13 to $18/bbl) gives 0.206 billion barrels of additional crude oil. Increasingly higher crude oil prices are required to produce additional increments of crude oil from new reserves in the lower 48 states; however, the relative increase in the quantity supplied is less than the relative increase in the price.

In 1995, increasingly higher crude oil prices are again required to produce additional increments of crude oil from new reserves in the lower 48 states. However, increasingly greater quantities of crude oil are produced at each price in the range from $8 to $18/bbl in 1995 than in 1985. The supply of crude oil from new reserves in the lower 48 states shows a higher response to price and a greater elasticity to price for 1995 than for 1985 because of the drilling capacity limitation in the model.

With the crude oil price fixed at $14/bbl (and natural gas liquid at $9.76/bbl) and with Case I conditions otherwise, economic supplies of natural gas from new reserves in the lower 48 states are shown in Figure 5-17 for 1985 and 1995. In 1985, the supply curve shows 3.53 trillion cubic feet of natural gas will be produced at $.60/Mcf. This supply curve further shows 8 trillion cubic feet of natural gas will be produced at $1.30/Mcf, and 11.3 trillion cubic feet of natural gas will be produced at $2/Mcf. Incrementally, the first $.70 increase (from $.60 to $1.30/Mcf) gives 4.47 trillion cubic feet of additional natural gas; the second $.70 increase (from $1.30 to $2/Mcf) gives 3.3 trillion cubic feet of additional natural gas. Increasingly higher natural gas prices are required to produce additional increments of natural gas from new reserves in the lower 48 states; however, the relative increase in the quantity supplied is greater than the relative price increase in the range from $.60 to $2/Mcf.

In 1995, increasingly higher natural gas prices are required to produce additional increments of natural gas from new reserves in the lower 48 states. However, as for crude oil, increasingly greater quantities of natural gas are produced at each price in the range from $.60 to $2/Mcf in 1995 than in 1985.

Figure 5-18 shows the crude oil supply curves estimated for 1985 in the present study and in two studies by FEA (1974, 1976). The FEA reported smaller crude oil supplies at different comparable prices in its 1976 study than in its 1974 study. However, Kim's estimates of crude oil supplies are generally smaller and less sensitive to price than FEA's 1976 estimates. This seems to have resulted from the much higher depletion rates assumed in FEA's studies.

A similar comparative plot of natural gas supply curves for 1985 is provided in Figure 5-19. Kim's curve generally falls between FEA's optimistic curve for 1974 and FEA's pessimistic curve for 1976. At the current regulated $1.45/Mcf, Kim's results indicate 8.6 trillion cubic feet of natural gas will be produced in the lower 48 states from new reserves. This result compares with an estimate of 6.3 trillion cubic feet from FEA's 1976 supply curve.

With reference to Case I, Figure 5-20 shows how the more favorable tax provisions of Case III shift the supply curve for crude oil to the right and how the lower finding rates of Case II shift the supply curve for crude oil to the left. Figure 5-20 also shows how the less favorable tax provisions of Case IV shift the supply curve for crude oil to the left from the position in Case II. As an illustration, the crude oil price required to bring forth a crude oil supply of 0.35 billion barrels in 1985 is $11.40/bbl in Case I without a depletion allowance and $9.75/bbl in Case III with a 22% depletion allowance.

Similarly, Figure 5-21 shows the price of natural gas required to produce 7 trillion cubic feet of non-associated gas from new reserves in the lower 48 states is $1/Mcf in Case III with a 22% depletion allowance and $1.13/Mcf in Case I with no depletion allowance. Figure 5-21 further shows the price must be increased to $1.28/Mcf to produce 7 trillion

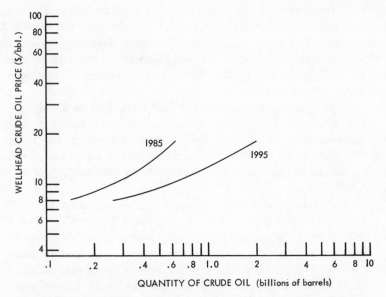

Figure 5-16. Economic supplies of crude oil from new reserves in the lower 48 states in 1985 and 1995 at a fixed wellhead natural gas price of $1.40/Mcf.

cubic feet in Case II, where a low finding rate projection basis is assumed. With amortization of intangible and dry-hole drilling costs in Case IV, a still higher price of $1.52/Mcf is required to produce 7 trillion cubic feet of gas.

5.6. Supply Functions for Crude Oil and Natural Gas from New Reserves in Texas

Economic supplies of crude oil and natural gas from new reserves in Texas were a regional subcomponent of the estimates developed for the lower 48 states in Section 5.4. Figures 5-22 and 5-23 show the Texas economic supply curves for crude oil and natural gas in 1985 and 1995, respectively; Case I conditions for tax provisions, finding rate projections, and drilling capacity limitations were assumed; also, the natural gas price was fixed at $1.40/Mcf.

(text continued on page 71)

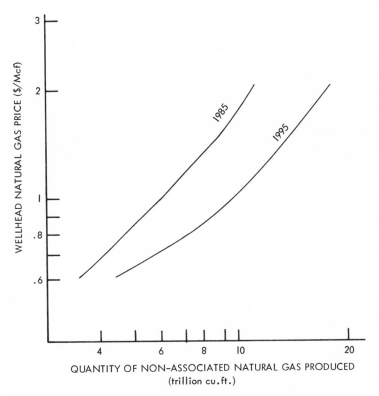

Figure 5-17. Non-associated natural gas supply curves in the lower 48 states from new reserves at a fixed wellhead price of $14/bbl (natural gas liquid price of $9.76/bbl).

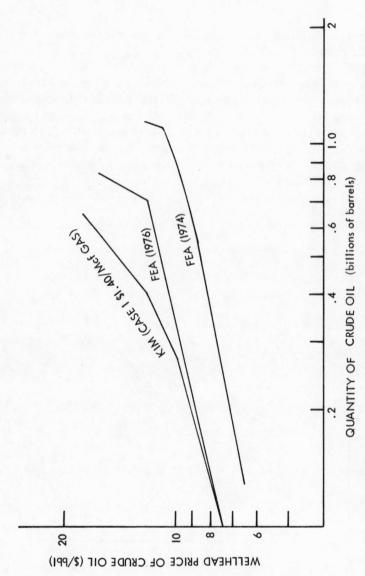

Figure 5-18. 1985 crude oil supply curves from new reserves in the lower 48 states from Federal Energy Administration and University of Houston studies.

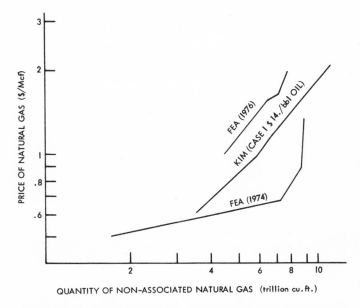

*Figure 5-19. 1985 natural gas supply curves from new dis-
coveries of non-associated gas in the lower 48 states from
Federal Energy Administration and University of Houston
studies.*

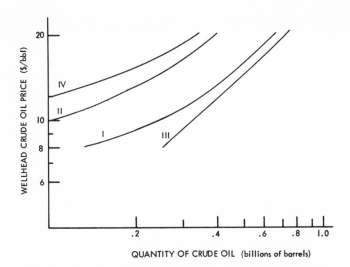

*Figure 5-20. Crude oil supply curves from new reserves in
the lower 48 states in 1985 for Cases I, II, III, and IV at a fixed
wellhead gas price of $1.40/Mcf.*

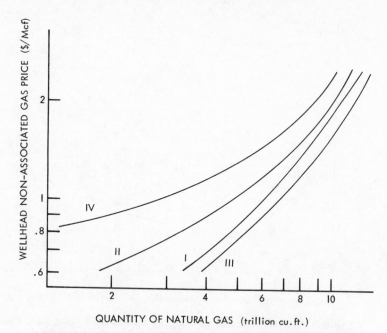

QUANTITY OF NATURAL GAS (trillion cu. ft.)

Figure 5-21. Non-associated natural gas supply curves from new reserves in the lower 48 states for Cases I, II, III, and IV at a fixed wellhead crude oil price of $14/bbl (natural gas liquid price of $9.76/bbl).

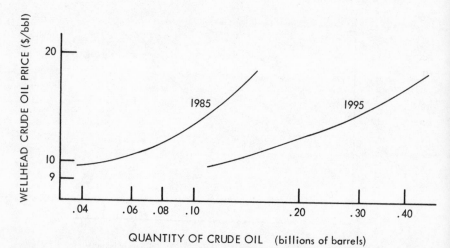

QUANTITY OF CRUDE OIL (billions of barrels)

Figure 5-22. Crude oil supply curves from new reserves in Texas at a fixed wellhead associated gas price of $1.40/Mcf (for 1985 and 1995). Case I conditions for tax provisions, finding rate projections, and drilling capacity limitations.

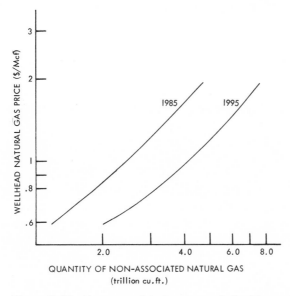

Figure 5-23. Non-associated gas supply for Texas from new reserves at fixed wellhead crude oil price of $14/bbl (for 1985 and 1995). Case I conditions for tax provisions, finding rate projections, and drilling capacity limitations.

In 1985, 46 million barrels of crude oil from new reserves are projected at $10/bbl; 111 million barrels are projected at $14/bbl; and 150 million barrels are projected at $18/bbl. Increasingly higher crude oil prices are required to produce additional increments of crude oil from new reserves in Texas, as in the lower 48 states.

In 1995, 107 million barrels of crude oil from new reserves are projected at $10/bbl; 283 million barrels are projected at $14/bbl; and 451 million barrels are projected at $18/bbl. Again, increasingly higher crude oil prices are required to produce additional increments of crude oil from new reserves in Texas; however, the crude oil supply response to price is increasingly greater at every price from $10 to $18/bbl in 1995 than in 1985.

With respect to the absolute quantities involved, the estimates of the economic supply curves for natural gas in Texas are much more interesting than the results for crude oil. In 1985, 1.25 trillion cubic feet of natural gas from new non-associated natural gas reserves are projected at $.60/Mcf; 3 trillion cubic feet are projected at $1.30/Mcf; and 4.5 trillion cubic feet are projected at $2/Mcf. Increasingly higher gas prices are required to produce the sizeable additional increments of non-associated natural gas from new reserves in Texas. The increase from $.60 to $1.30/Mcf increases the quantity supplied by 2.4-fold while the increase from $1.30 to $2/Mcf increases the quantity supplied by 1.5-fold.

In 1995, the quantity of natural gas supplied at $.60/Mcf (1.95 Tcf), $1.30/Mcf (5 Tcf), and $2/Mcf (7.12 Tcf) is significantly greater than the quantity supplied in 1985 at these prices. As for crude oil, increasingly greater sensitivity of the natural gas supply is found at higher gas prices in 1995 than in 1985. Relatively long time periods are required for supply adjustments to price to materialize in both crude oil and natural gas production.

Figure 5-24 shows how much reinstitution of the 22% depletion allowance in Case III would expand the supply curve for crude oil in Texas from the level of Case I, where no depletion allowance is assumed. Also, the supply curve of Case II shows how much the low finding rate basis would contract the supply curve for crude oil in Texas from the higher finding rate basis of Case I. In addition, the supply curve of Case IV shows the additional contraction from Case II of legislation to amortize intangible and dry-hole drilling costs. Clearly, a possible error in the finding rate for Texas crude oil has the largest shift effect of the cases illustrated.

Similar shift effects on the supply curves for natural gas in Texas are shown in Figure 5-25 for Cases I, II, III, and IV. Amortization of in-

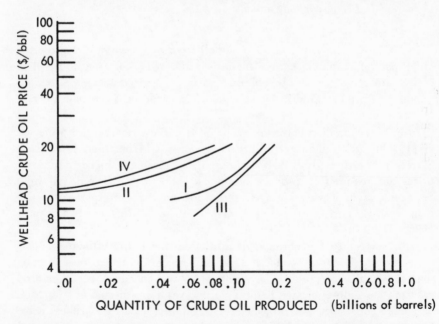

Figure 5-24. 1985 Texas crude oil supply curves from new reserves for Cases I, II, III, and IV at fixed wellhead natural gas price of $1.40/Mcf.

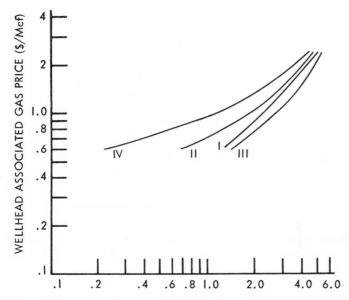

QUANTITY OF NON-ASSOCIATED NATURAL GAS PRODUCED (trillion cu. ft.)

Figure 5-25. 1985 Texas gas supply curves from new reserves for Cases I, II, III, and IV at fixed wellhead crude oil price of $14/bbl.

tangible and dry-hole drilling costs has the greatest shift effect. This shift is particularly evident for natural gas prices below $1.45/Mcf (the current regulated price).

The results in Figure 5-25 show the natural gas price must increase from $1.08/Mcf in Case III to $1.31/Mcf in Case I to produce 3 trillion cubic feet; they further show the price must increase from $1.31/Mcf in Case I to $1.42/Mcf in Case II to cover the costs of a low finding rate; also they show the price must increase from $1.42/Mcf in Case II to $1.67/Mcf in Case IV to cover the costs of disallowing current deductions for intangible and dry-hole drilling costs. Hence, the marginal costs of producing 3 trillion cubic feet of natural gas (non-associated) could increase by $.59/Mcf because of resulting policy modifications and finding rates.

6

Production Paths for Total U.S. Crude Oil and Natural Gas

The total U.S. production of crude oil represents: (1) production of crude oil from new reserves in the lower 48 states; (2) production of crude oil from old reserves (discovered before January 1, 1974) in the lower 48 states, offshore areas of the contiguous 48 states and Alaska, and southern Alaska; (3) production from new discoveries in offshore areas and southern Alaska; and (4) production from new and old discoveries in the North Slope of Alaska. Estimates of crude oil production from new reserves in the lower 48 states are augmented in this chapter with estimates of crude oil production for categories (2), (3), and (4). This augmentation relies heavily on the results of previous API and FEA data cited in this chapter. A similar procedure was used to obtain the total production of natural gas.

6.1. Production from Old Reserves Discovered Before January 1, 1974

Production from old reserves (the lower 48 states, southern Alaska, and offshore areas of the contiguous 48 states and Alaska) are based on 1974 reserve estimates and depletion rates. Enhanced recovery of crude oil from these reserves is based on estimates by FEA (1976) and ERDA (*Oil and Gas Journal*, Nov. 22, 1976).

The ultimate production from old reserves is the sum of production from "measured" reserves and the future growth of these reserve estimates. Table 6-1 summarizes measured reserves for crude oil, natural gas liquids, and natural gas (non-associated and associated), estimated by the API (1975) for the lower 48 states, southern Alaska, and offshore areas as of December 31, 1974. Reserve estimates for onshore Texas and offshore Texas are also listed. Since January 1, 1974, is the starting time for new explorations in our study, the measured reserves as of December 31, 1973, are adjusted for production during 1974; see Table 6-2.

By adding the measured reserve estimates for December 31, 1974, to the production in 1974, the measured reserve estimates for December 31, 1973, are obtained; see Table 6-3. The annual depletion rates for these measured reserves as of December 31, 1973, are obtained by dividing 1974 production by the reserve estimates as of December 31, 1973. These annual depletion rates, which are about 10% of the remaining reserves, are listed in Table 6-4. The same annual depletion rates are assumed to apply to these reserves in the future.

The measured reserve estimates for crude oil grow over time through revisions and extensions. This growth in reserves is largely the result of new exploratory drilling, development drilling, and the production history. As discussed in Chapter 3, the growth of non-associated gas reserves is primarily due to additional exploratory drilling.

The estimates for the growth of crude oil are the sum of the indicated reserves and 25% of the inferred reserves estimated by the USGS as of December 31, 1974 (Miller et al., 1975); see column 1 of Table 6-5. Following the adjustment procedure for estimating the measured reserves, the estimates for indicated and inferred reserves are adjusted by adding the reserve growth during 1974 due to factors other than exploratory drilling in 1974. The reserve growth in 1974 was 25% of the new revisions and extensions published by API. The last column in Table 6-5 lists future crude oil reserve growth estimates for different regions as of December 31, 1973. Our study assumes the ultimate reserve growth will be spread evenly over the 10-year period from January 1, 1974, through December 31, 1983. This means 10% of the reserve growth estimates as of December

Table 6-1. Measured Reserves as of December 31, 1974*

Region	Crude Oil (10⁹ bbl)	Natural Gas Liquid (10⁹ bbl)	Non-Associated Gas (Tcf)	Associated Gas (Tcf)
Lower 48 States	21.086	5.534	126.228	39.752
Southern Alaska	0.146	0.0	0.628	0.078
Alaska Offshore	0.560	0.0	0.625	0.108
Pacific Offshore	0.858	0.0	0.0	0.463
Gulf of Mexico	2.212	0.816	30.874	4.474
Atlantic Offshore	0.0	0.0	0.0	0.0
Texas Onshore	10.996	2.791	54.197	22.656
Texas Offshore (State)	0.00197	0.00404	0.565	0.063

* Data source: API Reserve Estimates, May 1975.

Table 6-2. Production During 1974*

Region	Crude Oil (10⁹ bbl)	Natural Gas Liquid (10⁹ bbl)	Non-Associated Gas (Tcf)	Associated Gas (Tcf)
Lower 48 States	2.533	0.616	13.438	3.611
Southern Alaska	0.015	0.0	0.0628	0.0078
Alaska Offshore	0.056	0.0	0.0625	0.0108
Pacific Offshore	0.082	0.0	0.0	0.030
Gulf of Mexico	0.358	0.108	3.528	0.567
Atlantic Offshore	0.0	0.0	0.0	0.0
Texas Onshore	1.226	0.333	6.035	1.791
Texas Offshore (State)	0.00016	0.00033	0.043	0.0002

Data Source: API Reserve Estimates, May 1975.

Table 6-3. Measured Reserves as of December 31, 1973*

Region	Crude Oil (10⁹ bbl)	Natural Gas Liquid (10⁹ bbl)	Non-Associated Gas (Tcf)	Associated Gas (Tcf)
Lower 48 States	23.619	6.150	139.666	43.363
Southern Alaska	0.161	0.0	0.691	0.08
Alaska Offshore	0.616	0.0	0.688	0.119
Pacific Offshore	0.940	0.0	0.0	0.493
Gulf of Mexico	2.570	0.924	34.402	5.041
Atlantic Offshore	0.0	0.0	0.0	0.0
Texas Onshore	12.222	3.124	60.232	24.447
Texas Offshore (State)	0.00213	0.0044	0.608	0.063

* Data Source: API (1975), Miller et al. (1975).

Table 6-4. Annual Depletion Rates for Measured Reserves*

Region	Crude Oil (10⁹ bbl)	Natural Gas Liquid (10⁹ bbl)	Non-Associated Gas (Tcf)	Associated Gas (Tcf)
Lower 48 States	0.1072	0.1002	0.0962	0.0833
Southern Alaska	0.0932	†	0.0909	0.0909
Alaska Offshore	0.0909	†	0.0909	0.0909
Pacific Offshore	0.0872	†	†	0.0609
Gulf of Mexico	0.1393	0.1169	0.1026	0.1125
Atlantic Offshore	†	†	†	†
Texas Onshore	0.1003	0.1066	0.1002	0.0733
Texas Offshore (State)	0.0747	0.0750	0.0707	†

* Data Source: API (1975).
† No depletion rate is assigned because reserves are negligible.

**Table 6-5. Future Reserve Growth of Crude Oil Reserves for
Existing Reserves (10⁹ bbl)***

Region	Estimates as of December 31, 1974	Reserve Growth During 1974	Estimates as of December 31, 1973
Lower 48 States	7.890	0.391	8.281
Southern Alaska	0.051	0.006	0.057
Alaska Offshore	0.197	0.019	0.216
Pacific Offshore	0.308	0.0159	0.324
Gulf of Mexico	0.650	0.037	0.687
Atlantic Offshore	0.0	0.0	0.0
Texas Onshore	3.568	0.114	3.682
Texas Offshore (State)	0.00037	0.000014	0.000384

* Data source: API (1975), Miller et al. (1975).

31, 1973, is added to the remaining reserves at the end of each year, starting in 1974, to estimate the production level of the following year.

The last source of crude oil supply from old reserves is from enhanced recovery projects in the lower 48 states. The FEA estimated additional production from secondary and tertiary recovery projects; they assumed secondary recovery out of inferred reserves. However, inferred reserves are accounted for by reserve gowth (25%) and new exploratory drilling (75%) in our study; hence, only tertiary recoveries are added.

The FEA's (1976) Business-As-Usual scenario gives crude oil production of 0.4, 0.9, and 1.3 million barrels per day in 1980, 1985, and 1989. The ERDA (*Oil and Gas Journal,* Nov. 22, 1976) suggested these estimates may be too optimistic. The ERDA estimated production from tertiary recovery projects in 1985 to be 0.5 million barrels per day; this represents an increase of 0.25 million barrels per day from the 1976 level.

The tertiary oil production path from old reserves (discovered before January 1, 1974) used in our study is the solid line in Figure 6-1. This path assumes tertiary oil recovery (1) increases from 0.25 million barrels per day in 1976 to 0.80 million barrels per day in 1984, (2) holds constant at 0.80 million barrels per day from 1984 through 1988, and (3) declines linearly from 0.80 million barrels per day from December 31, 1984, to zero on January 1, 1995. Total crude oil reserve additions for this production path are 3.7 billion barrels. (Enhanced recovery from new reserves after January 1, 1974, is given by the supply model for onshore production in the lower 48 states.)

Additional associated natural gas production from the tertiary recovery projects considered here were assumed to be 1 Mcf/bbl of crude oil production.

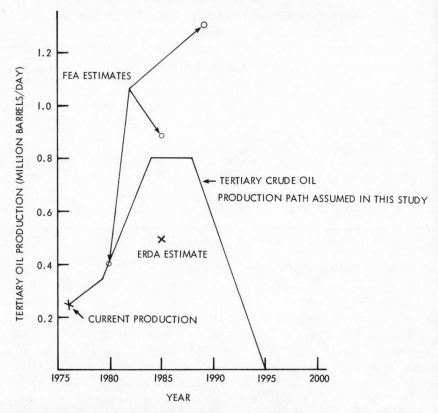

Figure 6-1. Production path for tertiary oil recoveries from old reserves prior to January 1, 1974.

6.2.   Production from New Alaska and Offshore Reserves

Production from new Alaska and offshore reserves represents production from reserves found after January 1, 1974, in southern Alaska and off-shore areas of Alaska and the contiguous 48 states (frontier areas). Productions from new discoveries in the frontier areas are based on USGS reserve estimates for undiscovered recoverable reserves and assumed production paths from these reserves; see Table 6-6.

For crude oil, undiscovered recoverable reserves and 75% of inferred reserves are added to total new reserve additions by exploratory drilling after January 1, 1974. For non-associated natural gas, all inferred reserves are added to the undiscovered recoverable reserves.

Production of associated gas is estimated from the regional gas-to-oil ratios (GOR) given in Table 6-7. Similarly, production of natural gas liquids is estimated from the oil-to-gas ratios (OGR) given in Table 6-7.

With estimates of additional reserves from new exploration, the next task is to derive production paths from these reserves. Figure 6-2 shows the two production paths assumed in our study. Production Path A shows a rapidly increasing production in the first 10 years; this path peaks at an 8% annual production rate from ultimate reserves and declines at a rate of 10% per year from the previous year's production starting in the twelfth year. Production continues for 32 years before depleting the reserves.

The increasing phase of production in the frontier areas is patterned after the increasing phase of production in the Gulf of Mexico. Production peaked in the Gulf of Mexico in 1971, 20 years after significant production began. However, future development in frontier areas is assumed to reach peak production after only 10 years, because of increased demand for crude oil.

Table 6-6. Recoverable Reserves of Crude Oil and Non-Associated Gas from New Discoveries in Frontier Areas*

Region	Crude Oil (10^9 bbl)	Non-Associated Gas (Tcf)
South Alaska	1.9	2.98
Gulf of Alaska	2.575	5.0
Bristol Bay	2.0	4.4
Pacific Offshore	3.15	0.874
Gulf of Mexico	6.8	106.086
Atlantic Offshore	3.0	7.6

* Data source: Miller et al. (1975).

Table 6-7. Gas Oil Ratio (GOR) for Estimating Associated Gas Production and Natural Gas Liquid Ratio (OGR) for Estimating Natural Gas Liquid Production In Frontier Areas*

Region	GOR (Mcf/bbl)	OGR (bbl/Mcf)
South Alaska	0.802	0.0344
Gulf of Alaska	0.802	0.0344
Bristol Bay	0.802	0.0344
Pacific Offshore	0.802	0.1185
Gulf of Mexico	1.605	0.0276
Atlantic Offshore	0.800	0.0329

* Data source: API (1975), Miller et al. (1975).

Production Path B assumes peak production will be reached in 15 years. This production path levels at 5.8% of annual production from ultimate reserves for 5 years, followed by a decline of 10% per year. It terminates 37 years after the start of production.

The areas under the two production paths give the same production from new reserves in the frontier areas. Production Path A was used to estimate crude oil production in all areas and natural gas production in all areas except the Gulf of Mexico; Production Path B was used to estimate non-associated gas production in the Gulf of Mexico because of its large undiscovered reserve potential.

The last task in determining future production for the frontier areas is to estimate the first year of production from new reserves in these areas. This onset of production is closely tied to the leasing schedule for oil and gas exploration in these frontier areas (*Oil and Gas Journal*, Sept. 13, 1976). Estimates of first year production from new reserves in frontier areas are given in Table 6-8.

Finally, note that the reserve estimates in Table 6-7 are based on water depths up to 600 ft. Also, no explicit economic analysis was made. Like the case for the onshore 48 states, future reserve additions in these frontier areas will depend on petroleum prices and cost of exploration, development, and production from these additional reserves. Potential reserve additions in deeper waters and changing reserve sizes due to changing costs and product prices should be considered for a valid long-range projection

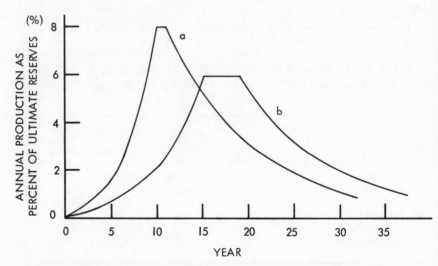

Figure 6-2. Production paths for new reserves from frontier areas.

of new petroleum supplies from these important frontier areas. Our study does not intend to investigate these problems; hence, the supply levels based on various assumptions set out in this chapter must be regarded only as a first approximation to future levels of production from these new frontier areas.

6.3. Production from the North Slope of Alaska

Crude oil production from the North Slope of Alaska and the Beaufort Sea will be limited by the transmission capacity of the trans-Alaska pipeline. Production paths for the North Slope and Beaufort Sea were estimated by FEA (1976) for three different scenarios (pessimistic, business-as-usual and optimistic); see Table 6-9. Note that no natural gas productions from the North Slope or the Beaufort Sea were included in our study because no definite transportation method exists at present.

6.4. Production Paths for Total Oil Liquids and Total Natural Gas for the United States

Production from old reserves (existing prior to January 1, 1974) in the lower 48 states, offshore areas, and Alaska is added to the production from new reserves in the lower 48 states to estimate production of total oil liquids (crude oil plus natural gas liquids) for the U.S. between 1974 and 2002. Figure 6-3 shows production paths of total oil liquids for five different possibilities: (1) Case I with $14/bbl for crude oil and $1.40/ Mcf for natural gas; (2) Case I with $12/bbl for crude oil and $1.20/Mcf for natural gas; (3) Case II with $12/bbl for crude oil and $1.20/Mcf for natural gas; (4) Case III with $14/bbl for crude oil and $1.40/Mcf

Table 6-8. Estimated Year of First Production from New Reserves in Frontier Areas

Region	Year of First Production
South Alaska	1975
Gulf of Alaska	1978
Bristol Bay*	1985
Pacific Offshore	1977
Gulf of Mexico	1975
Atlantic Offshore*	1982

* Five-year lag time is assumed from leasing to start of production.

for natural gas; and (5) Case IV with $12/bbl for crude oil and $1.20/ Mcf for natural gas.

For all five cases, production of total oil liquids bottoms out in 1976 at approximately 3.5 billion barrels; production increases as North Slope oil comes on stream in 1977, and production from new reserves more than offsets the decline in production from old reserves. Production of total oil liquids peaks at the lowest level (4.38 billion barrels) in the earliest year (1984) in Case IV and at the highest level (5.05 billion barrels) in the latest year (1988) in Case III. These production peaks fall between FEA's

Table 6-9. Alternative Production Paths for North Alaska Crude Oil
(10^6 bbl/day)*

	Pessimistic	Business-as-Usual	Optimistic
1974	0.0	0.0	0.0
1975	0.0	0.0	0.0
1976	0.0	0.0	0.0
1977	0.0	0.603	0.670
1978	0.552	1.155	1.362
1979	1.069	1.414	1.690
1980	1.241	1.655	2.000
1981	1.397	1.793	2.690
1982	1.431	2.138	3.069
1983	1.569	2.586	3.207
1984	1.690	2.707	3.310
1985	1.879	2.793	3.379
1986	1.966	2.897	3.397
1987	2.172	2.810	3.345
1988	2.069	2.655	2.966
1989	1.966	2.517	2.655
1990	1.897	2.414	2.172
1991	1.793	2.207	1.655
1992	1.690	1.966	1.276
1993	1.552	1.690	0.970
1994	1.448	1.414	0.741
1995	1.345	1.190	0.586
1996	1.172	1.034	0.431
1997	1.000	0.879	0.328
1998	0.828	0.759	0.241
1999	0.690	0.638	0.190
2000	0.603	0.534	0.172
2001	0.500	0.434	0.154
2002	0.410	0.340	0.136

* Data source: FEA (1976).

business-as-usual (BAU) forecast (5.2 billion barrels) and FEA's pessimistic forecast (4.2 billion barrels) for 1985; see *National Energy Outlook* (FEA, 1976). Also, our study shows higher production levels in the mid-1980s than shown in *Exxon's Energy Outlook: 1975-1990* (Exxon Company, 1976).

For production from new reserves, as shown in Chapter 5, different tax provisions, price combinations, and finding rate projections result in strikingly different production paths for total oil liquids in the period following 1985. With the 22% depletion allowance and the high price combination ($14/bbl and $1.4/Mcf) in Case III, production of total oil liquids is slightly higher (3.88 billion barrels) in 2002 than in 1974 (3.8 billion barrels). Removing the depletion allowance and continuing the favorable prices reduces production of total oil liquids 22% from 3.9 billion barrels in Case III to 2.65 billion barrels in Case I. Reduction of the prices for crude oil ($14 to $12/bbl) and for natural gas ($1.40 to $1.20/Mcf) reduces production of total oil liquids another 0.53 billion barrels for the scenario of Case I in 2002. Assuming a low finding rate rather than a high finding rate projection basis (Case II vs. Case I) reduces production of total oil liquids still another 0.92 billion barrels in 2002. Discontinuing current deductions for intangible and dry-hole drilling costs decreases production of total oil liquids slightly (0.2 billion barrels) in Case IV from the already low level of Case II. Thus, the production

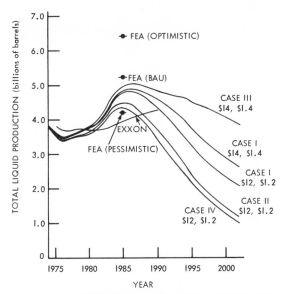

Figure 6-3. Production paths for total oil liquids (crude oil plus natural gas liquids).

of total oil liquids in the pessimistic scenario of Case IV is only 25% of the production of total oil liquids in the optimistic scenario of Case III.

The production paths for total natural gas (associated plus non-associated) in Figure 6-4 show production relationships similar to those for total oil liquids. Production of total natural gas is always the greatest for the optimistic scenario of Case III and is always the least for the pessimistic scenario of Case IV. In the optimistic scenario, production of total natural gas bottoms out in 1978 at 18.8 billion cubic feet; and production of total natural gas peaks in 1994 at 30.2 trillion cubic feet. In the pessimistic scenario, production of total natural gas bottoms out in 1983 at 16.2 trillion cubic feet; and production of total natural gas peaks in 1989 at 17.4 trillion cubic feet.

Exxon's path for total natural gas production generally follows the pattern of our path for total natural gas production in the pessimistic scenario. In 1985, FEA's forecast of total natural gas production in their pessimistic case (17.3 trillion cubic feet) slightly exceeds our forecast of total natural gas production in the pessimistic scenario (Case IV—16.7 trillion cubic feet). Also FEA's forecast of total natural gas production in their Business-As-Usual case (22.3 trillion cubic feet) nearly equals our forecast of total natural gas production in the optimistic scenario (Case III—22.2 trillion cubic feet).

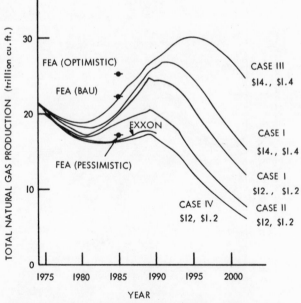

Figure 6-4. Production paths for total natural gas (associated gas plus non-associated natural gas).

As illustrated for total oil liquids production, different tax provisions, price combinations, and finding rate projections result in notably different production paths for total natural gas in the 1990s. In 2002, production of total natural gas is nearly four times greater in the optimistic scenario- (Case III—$14/bbl oil and $1.4/Mcf gas) than in the pessimistic scenario (Case IV—$12/bbl oil and $1.2/Mcf gas).

One salient feature of the production paths for total oil liquids and also for total natural gas is the slow production response to favorable tax and price incentives. For example, total natural gas production peaked at 22 trillion cubic feet in 1973 and has been decreasing ever since. With favorable incentives, 11 years (1973-1984) are required in our optimistic scenario (Case III—$14/bbl oil and $1.4/Mcf gas) to regain the production level observed in 1973.

6.5   Sources of Production for Total Oil Liquids and Natural Gas

Figure 6-5 shows the production for total oil liquids in the U.S. from all reserve sources between 1974 and 2002. As of January 1, 1974, production of total oil liquids from old reserves (discovered prior to that date) in the lower 48 states accounted for 85% of all U.S. production;

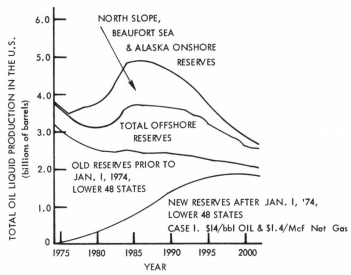

Figure 6-5. Total oil liquid production for the U.S. from all reserve sources.

most of the remaining 15% was produced from offshore reserves, largely in the Gulf of Mexico. Production of total oil liquids from these old reserves in the lower 48 states will represent a large, but continually declining, portion of U.S. production in the rest of the 1970s and the early 1980s.

Starting in late 1977, production of total oil liquids from the North Slope comes on rapidly to help offset the decline in production from old reserves in the lower 48 states. This partial offset is increasingly complemented by production from new reserves in the lower 48 states and from old and new reserves in the offshore areas.

In the peak year of production (1986), production of total oil liquids from new reserves in the lower 48 states and from old as well as new reserves in the offshore and Alaskan areas (frontier areas) represents two thirds of all U.S. production. Around 50% of the 1986 production comes from the frontier areas, where relatively large investments must be made and great risks must be undertaken to find, develop, and produce additional oil; only 17% of the 1986 production comes from new reserves (discovered after January 1, 1974) in the lower 48 states.

Production of total oil liquids from the frontier areas and the lower 48 states is projected (under the assumptions of our study) to decline continually after 1987. However, increased production of oil from new reserves in the lower 48 states becomes an increasingly important portion

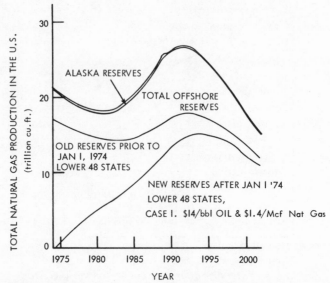

Figure 6-6. Total natural gas production in the U.S. from all reserve sources.

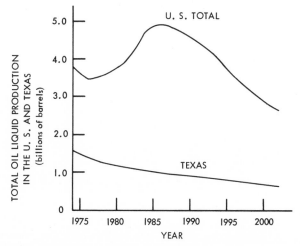

Figure 6-7. Total oil liquid production in the U.S. and Texas. Case I conditions for the lower 48 states at $14/bbl and $1.40/Mcf.

of this declining national production in the last part of the twentieth century. This growing source, which is the only one visualized as being stimulated by price and policy, represents 65% of total U.S. oil production in 2000.

If estimates of new reserves in the frontier areas are modeled as a function of price and policy, as modeled for the lower 48 states, then production of total oil liquids from the frontier areas would be expected to increase, rather than decrease, in the last part of the twentieth century. Investigation of this strikingly plausible possibility needs to be undertaken with dispatch and studied thoroughly before an irreversible energy policy is implemented to stimulate the development of alternative, higher-cost energy resources.

Figure 6-6 shows the total U.S. production of natural gas from all reserve sources between 1974 and 2000. This set of production relationships for gas differs in two distinct ways from the set of production relationships for oil. First, gas production from new reserves in the lower 48 states has enough supply potential to reverse in the late 1980s and early 1990s the current downward trend in production. Second, gas production from Alaskan reserves is regarded as negligible because no definite means of transportation is yet in sight for the large potential reserves of the North Slope and Beaufort Sea.

6.6. Production of Total Oil Liquids and Natural Gas in Texas and the United States

Figure 6-7 shows the production of total oil liquids in both Texas and the U.S. Figure 6-7 portrays a continually declining role for Texas in

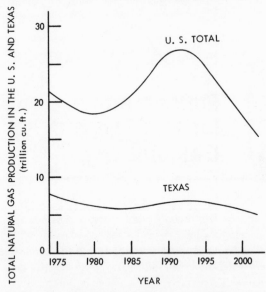

Figure 6-8. Total natural gas production in the
U.S. and Texas. Case I conditions for the lower 48
states at $14/bbl oil and $1.40/Mcf gas.

U.S. oil production; Texas production falls from 42% of the U.S. total in
1974 to around 20% in 1986.

Figure 6-8 shows the production of total natural gas in Texas relative
to the production of total natural gas in the U.S. Figure 6-8 indicates
a slightly brighter picture for Texas for the future production of gas
than for the future production of oil. Texas gas production remains
around 35% of U.S. gas production from 1974 through the early 1980s;
thereafter, its relative supply contribution decreases to 26% in the early
1990s, followed by an increase to 32% in 2002. In summary, Texas will
continue to be a mainstay supplier of gas to the nation for the rest of
the twentieth century.

Appendix I

Mathematical Expressions for Net Present Value Calculations

Appendix I derives formulas for net present value (NPV) calculations for oil and gas exploration, development, and production. Investment, depreciation of capitalized assets, and production of discovered reserves take place over three time periods: (1) The investment is assumed to spread equally over T_e years from the start of exploratory ventures; (2) depreciation of capital assets takes place over ten years or production years, whichever is shorter, after the onset of production; and (3) the production follows at the end of investment (T_e) and continues to $(T_e + T_a - 1)$ years for a total of $(T_a - 1)$ production years. The NPV calculations involve cash flow analysis for the total project years of $(T_e + T_a - 1)$ and discounted back to the present using the mid-year discount method.

I.1. Determination of Terminal Year of Production

The production terminates when the gross revenue of sale of produced oil and gas does not cover the royalty, state production tax, and production costs. The production will terminate at the end of $T_a - 1$, if

$$(1 - R - AST - VOPR)\, F \cdot \Delta Y \cdot d\, (1 - d)^{T_a - 1} < WOC \cdot NPV, \qquad (I-1)$$

where R is the royalty rate, AST is the state production tax rate, VOPR is the fraction of gross revenue to cover variable production cost, and F is the proceeds from production of one barrel of crude oil or 1 Mcf of non-associated gas.

For crude oil,

$$F = P_o + GOR \cdot P_g, \qquad (I-2)$$

and for non-associated gas,

$$F = P_g + 0.697\, P_o \cdot OGR, \qquad (I-3)$$

where P_o is crude oil price in \$/bbl, P_g is natural gas price in \$/Mcf, GOR is gas-oil-ratio in Mcf/bbl, and OGR is natural gas liquid production per Mcf of non-associated gas. Equation (I-1) tells that the production will be terminated at the end of $(T_a - 1)$ years from the start of production.

I.2.   Cash Flow Analysis

Cash outlay for a new exploratory venture includes (1) both capitalized (CAPI) and expensed investments (EXPI) equally over the first T_e years, (2) variable and fixed production costs, and (3) royalty and state production tax payments over $(T_a - 1)$ years starting the year of T_e.

Table I-1 summarizes annual cash outlay of $(CAPI + EXPI)/T_e$ over the first T_e years. Production expense includes a constant fraction (VOPR) of gross proceeds from sales of exponentially declining oil and gas production and fixed well operating costs.

Year of Production	Variable Production Expense
1	$F \cdot VOPR \cdot \Delta Y \cdot d$
2	$F \cdot VOPR \cdot \Delta Y \cdot d(1 - d)$
.	.
.	.
.	.
$T_a - 1$	$F \cdot VOPR \cdot \Delta Y \cdot d \, (1 - d)^{T_a - 2}$

The fixed well operating cost is the product of the number of producing wells (NPW) and annual well operating cost (WOC) in \$/yr/well:

$$NPW \cdot WOC$$

The number of producing wells is the sum of productive exploratory (NPEW) and development wells (NPDW).

Both royalty and state production tax are fixed fractions of gross revenue and are summarized in Table I-1. Discount factors are also shown for each year of cash outlay with a discount factor of r.

Cash inflow from the project is tax credit of $t_c \cdot CAPI/T_e$ for the first T_e years and gross revenue from sales of oil and gas. Depreciation and depletion allowances are noncash items but will be part of the profitability of the project when corporate income tax is calculated. Depreciation will be CAPI/YDEPR for YDEPR years after the start of production, and depletion allowance will be a constant fraction (d_a) of gross revenue. Table I-2 summarizes annual cash inflow from the project.

Table I-1. Cash Outflow Before Corporate Income Tax

Year	Discount Factor	Investment	Production Expense		Royalty	State Production Tax
			Variable	Fixed		
$0\sim1$	$(1+r)^{-0.5}$	$(CAPI+EXPI)/T_e$	0	0	0	0
$1\sim2$	$(1+r)^{-1.5}$	$(CAPI+EXPI)/T_e$	0	0	0	0
$\cdots$	$\cdots$	$\cdots$	$\cdots$	$\cdots$	$\cdots$	$\cdots$
$T_e-1\sim T_e$	$(1+r)^{-T_e+0.5}$	$(CAPI+EXPI)/T_e$	0	0	0	0
$T_e\sim T_e+1$	$(1+r)^{-T_e-0.5}$	0	$F\cdot VOPR\cdot\Delta Y\cdot d$	$WOC\cdot NPW$	$F\cdot R\cdot\Delta Y\cdot d$	$F\cdot AST\cdot\Delta Y\cdot d$
$T_e+1\sim T_e+2$	$(1+r)^{-T_e-1.5}$	0	$F\cdot VOPR\cdot\Delta Y\cdot d\cdot(1-d)$	$WOC\cdot NPW$	$F\cdot R\cdot\Delta Y\cdot d\cdot(1-d)$	$F\cdot AST\cdot\Delta Y\cdot d\cdot(1-d)$
$\cdots$	$\cdots$	$\cdots$	$\cdots$	$\cdots$	$\cdots$	$\cdots$
$\begin{bmatrix}T_e+T_a-2\sim\\ T_e+T_a-1\end{bmatrix}$	$(1+r)^{-T_e-T_a-1.5}$	0	$\left[F\cdot VOPR\cdot\Delta Y\cdot d\cdot(1-d)^{T_a-2}\right]$	$WOC\cdot NPW$	$\left[F\cdot R\cdot\Delta Y\cdot d\cdot(1-d)^{T_a-2}\right]$	$\left[F\cdot AST\cdot\Delta Y\cdot d\cdot(1-d)^{T_a-2}\right]$

$F = (P_o + P_g\cdot GOR)$ for oil

$F = (P_g + 0.697\cdot P_o\cdot OGR)$ for gas

NPW = Number of Productive Wells = NPEW + NPDW

Table I-2. Cash Inflow Before Corporate Income Tax

Year	Discount Factor	Tax Credit	Proceeds from Sale	Depreciation*	Depletion Allowance*
$0\sim1$	$(1+r)^{-0.5}$	$t_c \cdot CAPI/T_e$	0	0	0
$1\sim2$	$(1+r)^{-1.5}$	$t_c \cdot CAPI/T_e$	0	0	0
$\cdots$	$\cdots$	$\cdots$	$\cdots$	$\cdots$	$\cdots$
$T_e-1\sim T_e$	$(1+r)^{-T_e+0.5}$	$t_c \cdot CAPI/T_e$	0	0	0
$T_e\sim T_e+1$	$(1+r)^{-T_e-0.5}$	0	$F \cdot \Delta Y \cdot d$	CAPI/YDEPR	$F \cdot \Delta Y \cdot d \cdot d_a$
$T_e\sim T_e+2$	$(1+r)^{-T_e-1.5}$	0	$F \cdot \Delta Y \cdot d \cdot (1-d)$	CAPI/YDEPR	$F \cdot \Delta Y \cdot d \cdot (1-d) \cdot d_a$
$\cdots$	$\cdots$	$\cdots$	$\cdots$	$\cdots$	$\cdots$
$\begin{bmatrix} T_e+YDEPR-1\sim \\ T_e+YDEPR \end{bmatrix}$	$(1+r)^{-T_e-YDEPR+0.5}$	0	$F \cdot \Delta Y \cdot d \cdot (1-d)^{YDEPR-1}$	CAPI/YDEPR	$F \cdot \Delta Y \cdot d \cdot (1-d)^{YDEPR-1} \cdot d_a$
$\begin{bmatrix} T_e+YDEPR\sim \\ T_e+YDEPR+1 \end{bmatrix}$	$(1+r)^{-T_e-YDEPR-0.5}$	0	$F \cdot \Delta Y \cdot d \cdot (1-d)^{YDEPR}$	0	$F \cdot \Delta Y \cdot d \cdot (1-d)^{YDEPR} \cdot d_a$
$\cdots$	$\cdots$	$\cdots$	$\cdots$	$\cdots$	$\cdots$
$\begin{bmatrix} T_e-T_a-2\sim \\ T_e-T_a-1 \end{bmatrix}$	$(1+r)^{-T_e-T_a-1.5}$	0	$F \cdot \Delta Y \cdot d \cdot (1-d)^{T_a-2}$	0	$F \cdot \Delta Y \cdot d \cdot (1-d)^{T_a-2} \cdot d_a$

* non-cash contribution

d_a = depletion allowance (fraction of gross revenue)

I.3.   Net Present Value Calculations

Equation (2-12) in Chapter 2 is the basic equation for the NPV calculation:

$$NCF = NR + TC - CAPI - EXPI - t(NR - DP - DA - PE - EXPI) \qquad (2\text{-}12)$$

All variables are defined in Chapter 2.

After applying the annual discount factors, the corporate income tax outlay from investment (PV1) is given by:

$$PV1 = H[(1 + r)^{T_e + 0.5} - (1 + r)^{0.5}]/T_e \cdot r, \qquad (1\text{-}4)$$

$$H = (1 - t_c) \, CAPI + (1 - t) \, EXPI, \qquad (I\text{-}5)$$

where t is the corporate income tax rate.

The present value (PV2) of net revenue after royalty, state production tax, and variable operating cost is:

$$PV2 =$$
$$\frac{[(1 - t)(1 - R - AST) + t \cdot d_a - t \cdot VOPR](P_o + GOR \cdot P_g)d \cdot \Delta Y}{(d + r)(1 + r)^{T_e + 0.5}}$$
$$\times \, [1 - (1 - d)/(1 + r)^{T_a}] \qquad (I\text{-}6)$$

The present value from depreciation (PV3) is:

$$PV3 = [(1 + r)^{T_e + YDEPR + 0.5} - (1 + r)^{T_e + 0.5}]/r \times (t \cdot CAPI/YDEPR) \qquad (I\text{-}7)$$

Finally, the present value outlay (PV4) of fixed well operating cost is:

$$PV4 =$$
$$(t \cdot NPW \cdot WOC/r) \times [(1/[1 + r])^{T_e - 0.5} - (1/[1 + r])^{T_e + T_a - 0.5}] \qquad (I\text{-}8)$$

From Equations (2-12), (I-4), (I-6), (I-7) and (I-8), NPV for the project is given by:

$$NPV = PV2 + PV3 - PV1 - PV4 \qquad (I\text{-}9)$$

Appendix II

Derivation of Split Factors for Total Exploratory Drilling Footage into Oil and Gas Exploration

The exact mathematical procedure used to calculate the profitability index is described below; see Equation (II-15).

For crude oil discovery, the current net revenue per foot of exploratory drilling is:

$$NRV_o = (GOR \cdot P_g + P_o)(1 - R - AST_o + t \cdot DA)y_o, \qquad (II\text{-}1)$$

where R is royalty rates, AST_o is oil production tax rate, t is corporate income tax, DA is depletion allowance, and y_o is the average finding rate calculated from Equation (3-5).

For gas discovery,

$$NRV_g = (P_g + OGR \cdot P_l)(1 + R - AST_g + t \cdot DA)y_g, \qquad (II\text{-}2)$$

where AST_g is gas production tax, y_g is long-term average finding rate calculated from Equation (3-6), and P_l is the natural gas liquid price in $/bbl.

Drilling cost for successful oil well exploration and development cost (SDC_o) is:

$$SDC_o = (SRE + TDRO \cdot SRD)CDO, \qquad (II\text{-}3)$$

where SRE (SRD) is successful exploratory (development) drilling footage ratio, TDRO is the ratio of total oil well development drilling over exploratory drilling footage, and CDO is average oil well drilling and equipping cost.

For gas wells,

$$SDC_g = (SRE + TDRG \cdot SRD)CDG \qquad (II\text{-}4)$$

Drilling cost for unsuccessful oil well exploration and development is calculated:

$$USDC_o = CDD[1 - SRE + TDRO(1 - SRD)], \qquad (II\text{-}5)$$

where CDD is dry-hole cost.
Similarly, for gas wells,

$$USDC_g = CDD[1 - SRE + TDRG(1 - SRD)] \qquad (II\text{-}6)$$

The total drilling cost then is:

$$\begin{aligned} TDC_o &= SDC_o + USDC_o \\ TDC_g &= SDC_g + USDC_g \end{aligned} \qquad (II\text{-}7)$$

The intangible portion of successful oil wells is 0.7, while successful gas wells have an intangible portion of 0.73. Therefore, expensed intangible costs are:

$$\begin{aligned} ITDC_o &= IT_o \cdot SDC_o \\ ITDC_g &= IT_g \cdot SDC_g \end{aligned} \qquad (II\text{-}8)$$

The geological and geophysical exploration expenditures are:

$$\begin{aligned} GG_o &= 0.18\, TDC_o, \\ GG_g &= 0.18\, TDC_g, \end{aligned} \qquad (II\text{-}9)$$

of which the expensed portion is

$$\begin{aligned} GGED_o &= GG_o \cdot DDC_o / TDC_o, \\ GGED_g &= GG_g \cdot DDC_g / TDC_g, \end{aligned} \qquad (II\text{-}10)$$

primary lease equipment investments are

$$\begin{aligned} PLE_o &= 0.20\, TDC_o, \\ PLE_g &= 0.20\, TDC_g, \end{aligned} \qquad (II\text{-}11)$$

overhead expenditures for exploration and development are

$$\begin{aligned} OVHD_o &= 0.30\, TDC_o, \\ OVHD_g &= 0.30\, TDC_g, \end{aligned} \qquad (II\text{-}12)$$

Table II-1. Historical Exploratory Drilling Footages, Success Rates, Long-term Finding Rates, Average Drilling Costs,* Petroleum Prices,* Depletion Allowance, and Tax Credit Rate

Year	Exploratory Drilling Oil Well (1,000 ft)	Exploratory Drilling Gas Well (1,000 ft)	Success Ratio	Wellhead Oil Price ($/bbl)	Wellhead Gas Price ($/MCf)	Natural Gas Liquid Price ($/bbl)	Split Factor	Long-term Oil Finding Rate (bbl/ft)	Long-term Gas Finding Rate (Mcf/ft)	Oil Well Drilling Cost ($/ft)	Gas Well Drilling Cost ($/ft)	Depletion Allowance	Tax Credit Rate
1945	15,653	7,396	0.240	3.580	.1409	—	0.6791	—	—	26.80	35.72	0.275	0.0
1946	14,598	7,740	0.240	3.624	.1302	3.994	0.6535	178.12	1297.30	24.83	33.11	0.275	0.0
1947	18,296	8,097	0.234	4.038	.1255	4.659	0.6932	132.90	1149.94	21.86	29.14	0.275	0.0
1948	22,244	10,507	0.220	5.025	.1256	6.010	0.6792	106.88	1026.21	20.21	26.94	0.275	0.0
1949	24,769	10,029	0.240	5.169	.1282	5.212	0.7118	89.28	926.52	22.30	29.74	0.275	0.0
1950	29,906	10,269	0.229	4.913	.1272	4.521	0.7444	76.27	852.88	21.47	28.63	0.275	0.0
1951	38,168	11,176	0.215	4.445	.1282	4.355	0.7735	65.51	792.77	19.75	26.33	0.275	0.0
1952	39,410	15,755	0.214	4.573	.1410	4.326	0.7144	57.06	733.37	21.27	28.35	0.275	0.0
1953	42,536	17,824	0.221	4.912	.1686	4.616	0.7047	50.67	675.27	23.02	28.41	0.275	0.0
1954	40,206	18,799	0.232	5.084	.1847	4.145	0.6814	45.80	625.51	21.88	29.18	0.275	0.0
1955	45,945	22,223	0.231	5.050	.1914	4.136	0.6740	41.84	581.21	21.13	28.18	0.275	0.0
1956	49,691	23,159	0.219	4.928	.1907	4.226	0.6821	38.34	541.65	21.73	28.99	0.275	0.0
1957	48,826	25,484	0.228	5.303	.1939	3.964	0.6214	35.60	507.10	22.12	29.93	0.275	0.0
1958	37,020	23,254	0.231	5.093	.2013	3.980	0.6142	33.61	478.24	21.02	28.00	0.275	0.0
1959	36,143	25,514	0.230	4.898	.2178	3.972	0.5862	32.00	453.81	21.99	29.14	0.275	0.0
1960	30,169	24,151	0.220	4.859	.2362	4.039	0.5554	30.69	432.31	21.18	28.53	0.275	0.0
1961	28,103	25,002	0.205	4.895	.2558	3.629	0.5292	29.65	413.75	20.51	28.10	0.275	0.0
1962	28,180	23,555	0.212	4.898	.2618	3.617	0.5447	28.73	397.51	21.11	28.45	0.275	0.07
1963	30,516	20,141	0.199	4.895	.2678	3.344	0.6024	27.84	384.38	20.54	26.86	0.275	0.07
1964	32,417	20,294	0.197	4.869	.2601	3.337	0.6150	27.0 (34.4)**	373.3 (393.0)**	19.80	28.23	0.275	0.07
1965	27,080	18,958	0.185	4.741	.2587	3.401	0.5882	26.2 (33.9)	363.4 (382.9)	19.98	27.30	0.275	0.05
1966	27,806	23,083	0.195	4.621	.2520	3.591	0.5464	25.5 (33.3)	353.5 (372.5)	19.90	30.61	0.275	0.05
1967	26,524	18,739	0.208	4.676	.2624	3.698	0.5860	24.9 (32.6)	344.4 (363.0)	20.62	32.18	0.275	0.07
1968	27,767	18,304	0.164	4.591	.2656	3.214	0.6027	24.3 (32.0)	336.9 (355.2)	20.98	32.19	0.275	0.07
1969	30,991	23,542	0.220	4.646	.2647	2.841	0.5683	23.7 (31.4)	329.0 (346.9)	21.76	30.63	0.22	0.0
1970	24,570	17,865	0.193	4.798	.3330	3.045	0.5790	23.2 (30.9)	321.7 (339.2)	21.33	32.96	0.22	0.0
1971	19,492	17,474	0.174	4.796	.3446	3.129	0.5273	22.8 (30.5)	315.8 (333.0)	21.62	32.88	0.22	0.07
1972	19,767	22,679	0.191	4.556	.3347	3.049	0.4657	22.5 (30.1)	309.5 (326.3)	22.88	31.51	0.22	0.07
1973	16,209	25,957	0.224	4.625	.3306	3.494	0.3844	22.2 (29.8)	302.3 (318.7)	22.88	29.16	0.22	0.07
1974	18,520	29,285	0.249	6.740	.3700	4.601	0.3874	21.9 (29.5)	294.6 (310.7)	25.45	32.80	0.22	0.07
(1975)	22,675	27,792	0.235	7.127	.5583	—	0.4493	—	—	—	—	0.10	0.10

*All prices and costs are expressed in 1974 dollars. Wholesale price index was used

Table II-2. Data Used To Calculate Profitability Index

Items	Historical		Projected
	1946–1961	1961–1974	
Drilling Cost			
Oil well ($/ft)	Table II-1	Table II-1	25.45
Gas well ($/ft)	Table II-1	Table II-1	32.80
Dry well ($/ft)	0.76 × oil well	0.808 × oil well	21.79
	0.573 × gas well	0.577 × gas well	
Petroleum Prices			
Oil ($/bbl)	Table II-1	Table II-1	assumed values
Gas ($/Mcf)	Table II-1	Table II-1	assumed values
Natural gas liquid ($/bbl)	Table II-1	Table II-1	0.697 × crude oil price
Total Drilling Footage Ratio			
Oil	4.234	3.867	3.653
Gas	2.128	2.275	2.207
Dry Hole Ratio			
Development wells	0.250	0.250	0.249
Exploratory wells	0.785	0.785	0.800
By-products			
Associated gas (Mcf/bbl)	2.0	2.0	2.0
Natural gas liquid (bbl/Mcf)	0.0376	0.0376	0.0376
Tax Policies			
Royalties	0.125	0.125	0.125
Oil production tax	0.085	0.085	0.085
Gas production tax	0.120	0.120	0.120
Corporate income tax	0.50	0.50	0.50
Tax credit	Table II-1	Table II-1	assumed values
Depletion allowances	Table II-1	Table II-1	assumed values
Dry hole cost deduction	yes	yes	yes
Intangible drilling cost deduction	yes	yes	yes/no
Portion of intangible drilling cost:			
Oil	0.70	0.70	0.70
Gas	0.73	0.73	0.73
Other Expenses As Fraction of			
Total Drilling Cost:			
Geological and geophysical	0.18	0.18	0.18
Primary lease equipment	0.20	0.20	0.20
Overhead	0.30	0.30	0.30

and tax credits are

$$TAXC_o = t_c (PLE_o + SDC_o - ITDC_o),$$
$$TAXC_g = t_c (PLE_g + SDC_g - ITDC_g).$$ (II-13)

Total project cost after tax considerations is:

$$TC_o = TDC_o + GG_o + PLE_o + OVHD_o - t (ITDC_o$$
$$+ GGED_o + OVHD_o + USDC_o) - TAXC_o$$
$$TC_g = TDC_g + GG_g + PLE_g + OVHD_g - t (ITDC_g$$
$$+ GGED_g + OVHD_g + USDC_g) - TAXC_g$$ (II-14)

The relative profitability index (RPI) is defined as:

$$RPI = (NRV_o/TC_o) / (NRV_g/TC_g)$$ (II-15)

Table II-1 summarizes historical data for long-term finding rates, exploratory drilling rates, split factors, petroleum prices, drilling costs, depletion allowances, and tax credit. Other data used for calculating relative profitabilities in the past as well as in the future are summarized in Table II-2.

References

American Petroleum Institute, *Organization and Definitions for the Estimation of Reserves and Productivity Capacity of Crude Oil,* Technical Report No. 2, Division of Statistics, Washington, D.C., June 1970.

American Petroleum Institute, American Gas Association, and the Canadian Petroleum Association, *Crude Oil, Natural Gas Liquids, and Natural Gas in the United States and Canada and United States Productive Capacity as of December 31, 1974,* Vol. 29, May 1975.

American Petroleum Institute, Independent Petroleum Association of America, and Mid-Continent Oil and Gas Association, *Joint Association Survey of the U.S. Oil and Gas Producing Industry,* 1962-1975.

Baker, Warren L., "U.S. Drilling Activity in 1976 Likely to Experience Smaller Growth than in 1975," *Drilling Contractor,* Vol. 32, No. 1, January-February 1976.

Commoner, Barry, "A Reporter at Large, Energy-I," *The New Yorker,* February 2, 1976.

Dillon, E. L. and L. H. Van Dyke, "North American Drilling Activity in 1966," *The Bulletin of the American Association of Petroleum Geologists,* Vol. 51, No. 6, 1967.

Dix, F. A., Jr., "North American Drilling Activity in 1969," *The Bulletin of the American Association of Petroleum Geologists,* Vol. 54, No. 6, 1970.

Epple, Dennis N., *Petroleum Discoveries and Government Policy,* Cambridge, Massachusetts: Ballinger, 1975.

Erickson, Edward W. and Robert M. Spann, "Supply Response in a Regulated Industry: The Case of Natural Gas," *The Bell Journal of Economics and Management Science,* Vol. 2, No. 1, spring 1971.

Exxon Company, *Energy Outlook: 1975-1990,* December 1976.

Federal Energy Administration, *Project Independence,* Washington, D.C.: U.S. Government Printing Office, November 1974.

Federal Energy Administration, *1976 National Energy Outlook,* Washington, D.C.: U.S. Government Printing Office, March 1976.

Hausman, Terry A., "Project Independence Report: An Appraisal of U.S. Energy Need Up to 1985," *The Bell Journal of Economics and Management Science*, Vol. 6, No. 2, pp. 517-551, autumn 1975.

Hill, Robert R., Economic Supply Models for Crude Oil and Natural Gas in Texas, doctoral dissertation, University of Houston, May 1975.

Hubbert, M. K., "U.S. Energy Resources: A Review as of 1972," U.S. 93rd Congress, 2nd Session, Senate Committee on Interior and Insular Affairs, Serial No. 93-40 (92-75), 1974 .

Independent Petroleum Association of America, "Preliminary Cost Figures Show Sharp Increases in Well Costs," IPAA Cost Study Committee, *Drilling Contractor*, Vol. 32, No. 1, January-February 1976.

Inglehart, C. F. and F. A. Dix, Jr., "North American Drilling Activity in 1970," *The Bulletin of the American Association of Petroleum Geologists*, Vol. 55, No. 7, 1971.

Khazzoom, J. D., "The FPC Staff's Econometric Model of Natural Gas Supply in the United States," *The Bell Journal of Economics and Management Science*, Vol. 2, No. 1, pp. 51-93, spring 1971.

MacAvoy, Paul W. and Robert S. Pindyck, "Alternative Regulatory Policies for Dealing with the Natural Gas Shortage," *The Bell Journal of Economics and Management Science*, Vol. 4, No. 2, pp. 454-498, autumn 1973.

Miller, Betty M., et al., "Geological Estimates of Undiscovered Recoverable Oil and Gas Resources in the United States," Geological Survey Circular No. 725, March 1975.

National Petroleum Council, *U.S. Energy Outlook*, Washington, D.C.: U.S. Government Printing Office, December 1972.

Oil and Gas Journal, "ERDA Seen Developing Respect Between Industry and Government," Vol. 74, No. 47, pp. 176-177, November 22, 1976.

Oil and Gas Journal, "U.S. Falling Behind on OCS Lease Sales," Vol. 74, No. 42, pp. 42-43, September 13, 1976.

Oil and Gas Journal, "Researcher Defends Reserves Estimates," Vol. 74, No. 42, October 11, 1976.

Surratt, Marshall E. and A. Glynn Slaydon, "Comin' Up Roses (But Look Out for the Thorns)," *Drilling-DCW*, Vol. 36, No. 12, pp. 35-38, September 1975.

United States Department of the Interior, *Minerals Yearbook*, Washington, D.C.: U.S. Government Printing Office, 1947-1975.

Van Dyke, L. H., "North American Drilling Activity in 1967," *The Bulletin of the American Association of Petroleum Geologists*, Vol. 52, No. 6, 1968.

Van Dyke, L. H. and F. A. Dix, Jr., "North American Drilling Activity in 1968," *The Bulletin of the American Association of Petroleum Geologists*, Vol. 53, No. 6, June 1969.

Wagner, F. J. and C. F. Inglehart, "North American Drilling Activity in 1973," *The Bulletin of the American Association of Petroleum Geologists,* Vol. 58, No. 8, August 1974.

Wagner, F. J., "North American Drilling Activity in 1974," *The Bulletin of the American Association of Petroleum Geologists,* Vol. 59, No. 8, August 1975.

Index